A JOURNEY TO

Healing

YOUR

INNER CHILD

A JOURNEY TO

Healing

YOUR

INNER CHILD

A Practical CBT Workbook and Journal

*Unlock The Power to
Heal Emotional Triggers,
Overcome Past Traumas,
and Eliminate Fear of Abandonment*

Cameron J Clark

4 FREE GIFTS!

Are you ready to embark on a personal transformation journey? As a woman passionate about empowering others, I'm thrilled to offer you 4 free bonus eBooks that will propel your self-development.

By joining my email newsletter, you'll not only receive these valuable eBooks instantly but also gain access to a community dedicated to your growth. Expect personalized weekly tips, heartfelt insights, and empowering resources carefully *curated by me, Cameron J Clark.*

I believe in providing exceptional value to my community, which is why you'll also enjoy exclusive book giveaways, special discounts, and so much more. Best of all, your privacy is of utmost importance to me, and your email address is the only thing I'll ever ask for.

Don't miss out on this opportunity to invest in yourself and join a supportive community of like-minded women. Sign up today, and together, let's uncover the incredible woman within you!

To get your bonus, go to:
https://cameronjclark.com/Free-Gifts
Or scan the QR code below

- Escape the constant barrage of negative messages and take control of your thoughts.
- Transform beliefs into action: Rewire your thinking patterns to overcome self-limiting beliefs and unlock your true potential.
- Counter societal influences: Build self-acceptance, confidence, and resilience in the face of external pressures.
- Tap into ancient wisdom: Discover the timeless practice of affirmations for lasting personal transformation.
- Includes a Free Checklist as a Bonus.

Cultivate Inner Peace: Discover how acts of kindness can bring inner harmony and serenity, leading to a more fulfilling and joyful life.

- Nurture Authentic Connections: Explore how kindness fosters deeper connections with others, creating a network of support, love, and genuine relationships.
- Boost Your Well-Being: Learn how practicing kindness positively impacts your mental, emotional, and physical well-being, promoting a healthier and happier lifestyle.

- Experience Life-Changing Benefits: Discover how daily gratitude practice can bring happiness, reduce stress, improve relationships, and enhance overall well-being.
- Start a Gratitude Journal: Learn how to begin your gratitude journey by starting a journal to cultivate gratitude, shift your mindset, and invite positivity into your life.
- Deepen with Meditation: Enhance your gratitude practice through meditation, fostering inner peace, appreciation and amplifying the positive effects of gratitude in your daily life.

Harness the Power of Belief: Discover how cultivating empowering beliefs and positive thought patterns can align your mindset with manifestation, unlocking your true potential for success

- Visualization Techniques: Learn effective visualization techniques to vividly imagine and attract your desired outcomes, amplifying your manifestation abilities and bringing your dreams to life.

- Embrace Abundance Mentality: Shift from a scarcity mindset to an abundance mentality, embracing the belief that there are limitless possibilities available to you, allowing abundance to flow into your life.

Contents

Our thought patterns, feelings, and behaviors alike slowly come to resemble the toxic and harmful environments that surround us. It is a stark contrast to the loving life of a carefree child.

Introduction

CHILDREN ARE some of the most carefree creatures in the world. When I think of what it means to be a child, I think of so many beautiful things: chasing butterflies in an open garden, playing on swing sets, and lovingly bandaging their scraped knees. I imagine childhood, a carefree one, to be bedtime stories and lullabies, comfort and playtime. There's truly nothing like the experience of being a child when that experience blossoms naturally from a loving home. For a carefree child, there isn't a worry in the world, no bad memories to stick to you. Everything is a dream when you are a carefree child.

As children, we had such a beautiful view of the world. Naturally, children are very open and positive. Our worldview begins as something positive and wholesome, the healthiest our perspectives can ever be. But, over time, that begins to change. Hurtful events that we experience—both inside and outside of childhood—slowly take the center stage, shaping how we view everything around us. Our thought patterns, feelings, and behaviors alike slowly come to resemble the toxic and harmful environments that surround us. It is a stark contrast to the loving life of a carefree child.

Out of these two circumstances, I am willing to bet that you most resonate with the latter right now.

But, what if, all of the sudden, life presented you with a chance to truly heal. Would you take it?

Healing from the past can be one of the hardest things that we ever do in life. There are so many resources available for inner healing, many of which are incredibly easy to access, but we seem to always miss them. This happens because we either do not know about them or because we've lost hope that they would work in the first place. And it is completely valid to feel this way—to feel as though nothing in the world can right the wrongs you've faced and help you heal. It is important to me, however, that you know that no matter how difficult it gets, healing is always possible and worth a shot.

Even picking up this book in the first place is a major step forward. If no one else notices the effort you are making, I do. I notice the hard work you are willing to put in, the intention to change and make a difference in your life. You are making the right decision. While not a substitute for in-depth therapy, this book is a helpful tool in your healing journey.

In this all-new book to heal your inner child—the part of you containing the trauma, memories, and feelings associated with your childhood and childlike nature—and return to that innocent, carefree mindset you once had with the added integration of the ideas you've learned, you will uncover so many things. Namely, you will come to understand how to use skills from cognitive behavioral therapy (CBT) to your advantage, transforming the way that you handle mental health problems. You'll also learn relaxation and coping techniques and much more that will help you successfully regain contact with your inner child.

I encourage you to take the first step to healing by improving your ability to take charge of your thoughts and nurturing your relationship with your vulnerable parts, unlocking the gifts of the healed inner child in the process. Let's begin.

Chapter 1

Prerequisite Skills

AS YOU EMBARK on this healing journey, there are some skills that you will need and may not have already. These are known as the prerequisite skills—things you will have to master before we move forward. But do not worry, everything you need is provided for you all in one place.

Mindfulness

Mindfulness involves a sense of awareness regarding your surroundings and yourself, and it is the first skill you will need to familiarize yourself with. Simply engage in the provided activities and you will understand how mindfulness works and what being mindful feels like in your particular body.

Exercise No. 1 **Body Scan**

The goal of a body scan meditation is to increase the level of physical awareness you have, allowing you to remain present and in the moment. This is a common meditation tactic used to help with awareness, and you can perform a body scan as so (Aybar, 2021):

1. Get into a comfortable position, either sitting or lying down, and let your eyes close gently.

2. Begin with your focus on your lower body. If your feet are planted on the floor, take note of how they feel. Are they in pain, swollen, or otherwise notably hurting? Do you just feel them sitting there? Slowly, move your focus from your feet into your ankles, taking note of sensations like pressure, temperature, and tension as you do so. Once you've given your ankles a bit of attention, bring your mind up to the knees, and then the thighs, traveling up your body.

3. Once you are done with focusing on your lower body and releasing the tension in those areas, repeat the same process with your upper body, focusing on the abdomen, chest, arms, wrists, and hands as you do so. Be sure to note any sensations you feel as well as to release tension in the way we discussed in the last step. Take the time to notice your heart and lungs as well.

4. End the body scan by repeating this with your neck, face, and head overall. Remember to notice any sensations and release tension with your breath, just like we talked about.

And that is it! It is not a complicated process, but I'd like you to reflect on the following questions as well in order to process what you've just experienced.

In the space below, answer one or more of the following questions:

- Where did you notice the most tension in your body?

- Where did you notice the least tension?

- What do you think this exercise taught you?

Exercise No. 2 **Report Position**

The next exercise that we are going to focus on is called the report position. The report position is an exercise meant to encourage you to notice what you are doing in the current moment relative to what's going on around you. In other words, the report position helps you understand how you connect to your environment and what's going on right now. In order to engage with the report position exercise, you are going to have to be okay with feeling just a little silly. It is like a roleplay game, but I promise it is one of the most effective methods for tuning in to yourself and your surroundings.

To engage with the report position method, you are going to pretend that you are a secret agent. As a part of your mission, you need to describe your surrounding environment in as much depth as possible. In the space below, write down your observations:

_____

_____

_____

_____

_____

_____

_____

_____

_____

_____

Exercise No. 3 **Hands, Heart, Lungs**

The next activity that we are going to cover is called the hands, heart, lungs technique. The main goal of this exercise is to help you become aware of your body and how it sustains life.

In order to do this method, you need to go on a walk. So get outside and start walking. As you walk, pay attention to your breathing. Once you've given some attention to your breathing, focus on your heartbeat. Where can you feel your pulse the most? How fast is your heart going? Spend a few moments counting the steady rhythm of your heart rate as you continue to walk, really feeling each beat in the moment. Next, focus on your physical movements. Pay attention to how your feet strike the ground and any tension or movement of your muscles as you step.

After focusing on each of these things individually, I want you to try and focus on them altogether. Meaning, I want you to try and draw your focus to your hands, heart, and lungs all at the same time. Be kind to yourself if this doesn't come easily, and just keep trying.

Once you return home from your walk, answer some of these questions in the space provided:

- How was your walk?
- What did you notice about your body and your surroundings?
- What was easy for you to do, and what wasn't?
- How does this method differ from other walks you've taken?

Focus

The next prerequisite skill is focus. Focus is important to your inner child healing because it allows you to keep your mind on healing thoughts and the concepts you need to consider, rather than wandering into harmful or unproductive territory. These activities will help you perfect the art of remaining focused.

Exercise No. 4 **Still as Stone**

This next exercise is geared toward granting you the ability to improve your focus skills as a whole. For this focus exercise, I challenge you to sit as still as a stone. That is it! Try to sit still—absolutely still—for as long as you can. Set a stopwatch and truly see how long you can do so. Try not to allow your body to tense up while you engage with this exercise, as this can cause some pain.

After your time is up, fill out this table:

How many times did you try the exercise?	
What was the longest time you stayed as still as a stone?	
What parts of your body seemed to be the most active?	
Did you tense up as you held still?	
Record any additional observations:	

Exercise No. 5 Narrator's Lens

The goal of the narrator's lens activity with regard to focus is to help you maintain a level of awareness regarding what is going on in your headspace. In other words, this activity allows you to understand and notice what you are thinking and feeling internally. As the name of the activity suggests, you are going to pretend that you are a narrator in order to complete this exercise.

Imagine that you are narrating the internal workings of a character. Your job is to describe what is going on within their mind as if it were a movie scene or a part of a novel. In as much detail as possible, use what's going on in your mind to create this narration. Write it down below:

_____

_____

_____

_____

_____

_____

_____

_____

_____

_____

_____

_____

Exercise No. 6 **Lines and Colors**

This lines and colors exercise is another one meant to help you improve your ability to focus. I want to take a moment again to restate why being able to focus is so important. As you embark upon the process of recovery, you are going to have to focus on various things—from your mental state to activities and more. You'll need the ability to focus so that distracting or distressing thoughts can't take the forefront of your recovery process. It can be easy to let negative or unhelpful thoughts control us, which is why developing the ability to focus is so crucial to recovery—it allows you to make the active choice to focus on getting better.

For this exercise, I want you to follow these steps:

1. Pick an object that is sitting in the room with you. You can pick it up if you want, but I recommend allowing it to sit in good lighting on a surface nearby, allowing you to see it in good view. This is really important for the rest of your exercise.

2. Observe the object for a few minutes, taking in any edges, curves, colors, dents, or other features that make the object distinct.

3. Then, with your mind, trace the outline of the object one line at a time, almost as if you were drawing it. Go over the entire object in your mind slowly, until you have the outline of the object clearly in your mind.

4. Then, you are going to do the same thing but with colors. Copy the colors in your mind by placing them onto the image, as if you were coloring it in with a crayon or paints. Include the shades, taking note of how light hits the object.

5. If you are up for a challenge, you can finish the exercise by repeating the same thing on all sides of the object.

Once you have done this, complete this activity:

- The object I focused on was _____.

- It was harder for me to (draw the lines/color in the shape/ shade the shape) _____than it was to _____.

- During this activity, I felt _____.

- Something I noticed that I hadn't noticed about this object before is that _____.

- During this activity, I learned _____.

Breathing and Relaxation

After you've learned how to be mindful and remain focused, you need to be able to power through breathing and relaxation, even when it is hard. These exercises will guide you.

Exercise No. 7 **Conscious Breathing**

The next exercise that I want you to do is called conscious breathing, which is intended to allow you to control how you breathe in order to enter a state of relaxation. For this activity, I have a few different exercises that both fall under the umbrella of conscious breathing. The first one we'll cover is modified lion's breath.

Modified Lion's Breath

For modified lion's breath, you are going to follow these steps (Fowler, 2022):

1. Pretend you are a lion. You are going to be breathing like a lion's roar, so keep this image in your mind as you engage in the exercise.

2. Find a comfortable seat either on the floor or in a chair, allowing yourself to relax into its surface.

3. Breathe in deeply through your nose, allowing your air to fill your belly. If you'd like, you can place a hand on your stomach to help you feel the inflation occur.

4. As you come to a halt with your inhale, make sure that no more air can enter your lungs.

5. Open your mouth as wide as you can, and breathe out with a loud "HA" sound.

6. Repeat this exercise several times until you begin to feel more calm.

4–7–8 Breathing

The next breathing exercise we are going to do is called 4-7-8 breathing. It is another therapy and meditation approved method for controlling breathing, and this method is particularly effective when it comes to stopping a panic attack in its tracks. You can do 4-7-8 breathing by following these steps (Gotter, 2018):

1. Allow your lips to part gently and exhale everything in your lungs with a whooshing sound.

2. Now you are going to inhale. As you do so, count to four slowly and calmly in your head. Really take the time to focus on each number as you count upward.

3. For a count of seven, hold your breath in your lungs and notice how it feels to allow it to hover there.

4. With a whooshing sound again, exhale and count to eight.

5. Repeat at least ten times.

Both of these exercises are phenomenal for inducing calm and allowing you to control breathing, especially if you find yourself freaked out or incredibly anxious. Once you finish both of those activities, answer one or more of the following questions:

- How did you feel during each activity?
- Which activity did you like more and why?
- What was your favorite part of engaging in these two activities?

Square Breathing

Next, we have square breathing, which you'll complete in the following ways:

1. Close your eyes and visualize a square.

2. Inhale, and mentally trace one side of the square.

3. Hold your breath while tracing the top of the square, then exhale as you go down the other side.

4. Finally, pause as you trace the bottom of the square before starting over.

Once you've finished your square, answer these questions:

- I completed the square breathing exercise _____times.

- The square breathing exercise did the following to my breathing: _____.

- I found the square breathing exercise to be _____.

Exercise No. 8 **Somatic Exercise**

Another exercise that will help you through the process of breathing and relaxation is this somatic exercise I have for you. Somatic exercises are ones where your focus is directed internally rather than externally. The goal of this somatic exercise is to provide you with a somatic experience in order to release tension through the passageway it creates. You can engage in the somatic exercise as follows (Integrative Psychotherapy, n.d.):

1. The first thing that you are going to do is begin with a bit of mindfulness. Simply pay attention to yourself and your body, breathing in and out at a steady yet natural rhythm. Pay

attention to how you feel, how fast you are breathing, the rate of your heart, and the temperature. Spend a few moments focusing your awareness on how you feel.

2. Next, I want you to think back to a time you felt safe. In the recent past, when did you feel most calm and safe or most like yourself? Really consider this and allow yourself to feel one with that experience.

3. The next step is identification. Think back to the beginning of where you began to experience the most significant stressors of your childhood. It might be that you think about this in terms of an event, or you can consider this in correlation with what part of your body you began to feel the stress in. Either way, allow yourself to remember and reconnect to the source.

4. After that, you are going to replay what happened. Before you were stressed out and upset, you were calm. You are now going to replay the exact moment that you went from calm to stressed, allowing the images, actions, and words to flit through your mind like a slow movie. See if you can point out people, conversations, behaviors, and other concepts that caused you to feel stressed in that moment—anything that stands out as you replay the event.

5. As you continue to replay what happened, tune in to your body at that moment. Try to really embody how your physical body existed during this moment, tuning in to the sensations that you felt as you recall this event. Slow down as much as you need to. Notice if there's any change in how your body feels, a temperature shift, or anything else indicating that you feel stress or tension.

6. Finally, we are going to use a practice called healing hands. Place one or both hands gently on the area in which you

experienced the shift and breath gently. If you notice that your entire body feels a shift, you can simply place a hand over your heart. Breathe into this area of the body, envisioning the stress and tension being pushed out with every breath. Notice if anything comes into your consciousness that can offer clarity on the situation, but do not expect it. Just slow down and maintain awareness of your body.

Once you finish the exercise, answer the following questions:

- What was the stressful event that your mind focused on during the exercise?

- What sensations did you notice in your body before and after the exercise?

- What was the most difficult part of the exercise?

Exercise No. 9 Squeeze Release

The final relaxation exercise that I want to walk you through is one that I like to call the squeeze release, which mimics a commonly used relaxation technique called "progressive muscle relaxation." The idea is that by systemically tensing and then releasing the tension within your muscles, not only will they feel comparatively relaxed, but you will experience the release of tension that you didn't know you were holding. It also helps you gain control of your ability to relax. The squeeze release technique goes as so:

1. We're going to start with the very bottom of your body and then work upward; therefore, let's start with the feet. Tense your feet by clenching them—allowing your toes to curl in—tightly, and then release the pressure. Do the same in the opposite way by flexing your toes as widely as you can before releasing again.

2. Move up to your calves. Repeat the same thing, tensing your calves up before releasing as much tension as you can within that part of your body.

3. Take your attention up to your thighs, allowing them to tense up and then release the same way. Allow your focus to move up your body this way until you reach your arms, then work down them. Make sure to clench and stretch any part of your body that does both.

4. Work your way to your head and face, repeating the squeeze and release technique.

5. Finally, squeeze your whole body and then release—in whatever way that means to you.

Once you've finished, fill the following chart out based on how different parts of your body responded to the exercise:

Feet	
Calves	
Thighs	
Hips	
Stomach	
Hands	
Shoulders	
Chest	
Face	
This activity felt best in what part of the body:	

Thoughts as Thoughts

Finally, it is important to remember that thoughts are thoughts and nothing more. Let's explore this together.

Exercise No. 10 **Sitting Meditation**

Oftentimes, we give thoughts far more power than they deserve, allowing them to control our behaviors and perspectives on the world. It is important to be able to take a step back and realize that thoughts are just thoughts—they are internal considerations that do not have to be given the power to rule your life. This sitting meditation exercise is intended to help you disengage from your thoughts, recognizing them for what they are—just thoughts.

This will allow you to gain greater mental stability, the ability to let things go, and the capacity for insight and wisdom as well as compassion.

In order for you to engage in this sitting meditation, you are going to need about 40 minutes. For ten minutes each, you are going to envision the following scenarios (Bowdoin College, 2014):

1. Your thoughts are images that are being projected onto a movie screen. Imagine that your thoughts are movies or images projected like one. Notice how you can consider movie-like events to be real or you can take them for what they are— something fleeting that rises and moves away. Much like a movie, your thoughts are only temporary. Spend a few moments allowing your thoughts to play like a movie, watching them come and go without restraint.

2. Your thoughts are a performance on stage that you are watching from the audience. As you watch, pay special attention to how the performers on the stage act, or maybe even dance and sing. Notice how you get lost in what's going on the stage so easily—becoming so absorbed in something that is nothing more than a fleeting image, much like your thoughts.

3. Your thoughts are clouds floating through the spacious expanse of the sky within your mind. When we experience weather, we do not try to condemn it or hold onto it because that is not realistic. The weather isn't something that we can control. Similarly, your thoughts flow across the sky of your mind, some moving fast while others move slow, just like clouds. Simply notice the clouds and let them do what they will without judgment.

4. Your thoughts are leaves flowing along a running stream. Imagine your thoughts are leaves in a stream of water, floating

along. Connect this to yourself, realizing that your thoughts flow naturally with the current instead of controlling or fighting it—much like we should allow our thoughts to do in our minds.

Once you've spent about ten minutes with each visualization, you can answer whichever of the following questions you'd like to:

- Which visualization resonated the most with you?

- Which visualization did you like the least?

- What did you learn or what insight did you gain from the exercise?

Exercise No. 11 **Three-Minute Breathing Space**

The final exercise for this chapter is a breathing exercise that will allow you to check your thoughts and notice how they impact you (Bowdoin College, 2014):

1. During this exercise, you are going to simply watch the thoughts that come into your mind—not necessarily focusing on them or following them.

2. Start by reminding yourself that negative thoughts aren't factual; rather, consider them to be more like events that take place inside of your mind.

3. Write down your thoughts, either digitally or on paper. Writing our thoughts down is a really good method for seeing our thoughts in a way that is less overwhelming and more objective. Writing down a thought allows for us to separate it from ourselves, creating the chance for a more broad perspective. In other words, writing our thoughts down can create distance that is good for thinking logically.

4. Evaluate your thoughts closely. Try to recognize whether or not your thoughts fall into some of your commonly unhelpful patterns of thinking. For example, if you are prone to thinking things are much worse than they truly are, see if your thoughts fall into that pattern.

5. Focus on whatever emotions these thoughts are connected to, allowing yourself to fully embody the thought and concentrate on the emotion. Be kind to yourself as you do so.

Once you are finished, answer these questions:

- What thought did you find to be the most pressing?

- Were there any thoughts you tried to push out of your mind? What about ones you tried to cling to?

- What patterns did you recognize in your thinking?

Additional Activities

In addition to the activities provided thus far, I have various miscellaneous activities that can help you with this process. Throughout the course of your inner child healing, use these activities to soothe yourself, connect with yourself, and provide calm and peace to your inner child.

Inner Child Dialogue

Using the script spaces below, I want you to write a dialogue that represents a conversation between you and your inner child. The purpose of this is to allow you to communicate something that you think your inner child needs to hear. You can use this space to consider issues and emotions that arise over the course of talking to your inner child.

You :

Inner Child :

You :

Inner Child :

You :

Inner Child :

You :

Inner Child :

You :

Inner Child :

You :

Inner Child :

You :

Inner Child :

You :

Inner Child :

You :

Inner Child :

You :

Inner Child :

You :

Inner Child :

You :

Inner Child :

You :

Inner Child :

Once you are done, reflect on the experience. What was the most prominent emotion that came up during the experience, and do you believe this activity was fruitful in some way? Take some time to write about the experience below.

_____

_____

_____

_____

_____

_____

_____

_____

_____

_____

_____

_____

_____

_____

_____

_____

_____

_____

_____

Nature Exploration

As children, we tend to be very curious creatures—exploring nature and the world around us with a newfound hope and ambition, longing to see everything that's around us. How long has it been  since the last time you went outside just to explore?

I recommend doing this activity by collecting things if you can, but if you are in a public space, just observe. Try to find all of the following in nature, either outside of your home, at a park, or elsewhere.

1. Something red
2. Something orange
3. Something yellow
4. Something green
5. Something blue
6. Something purple
7. Something brown
8. Something white
9. Something black
10. Something hard
11. Something soft
12. A leaf
13. An acorn
14. An animal
15. A pathway
16. Something in the sky
17. A flower
18. Something man-made

Then, fill out the below chart with what you've collected and any observations about it:

OBJECT	OBSERVATIONS

Then, reflect on the activity:

- Doing the scavenger hunt made me feel_____.

- If my inner child could speak, I think they would say _____
  _____.

- When I was outside, I noticed_____.

Positive Affirmations

In my opinion, one of the most healing things that you can do is recite positive affirmations. If you say them enough, your brain slowly begins to believe them. Practice using the following inner child healing affirmations (Tewari, 2022):

1. I love and accept my inner child unconditionally.

2. I embrace the innocence and joy of my inner child.

3. I am deserving of happiness and playfulness in my life.

4. I release any wounds from my past and embrace healing for my inner child.

5. I am allowed to express my emotions freely and without judgment.

6. I give myself permission to dream and imagine without limitations.

7. I trust my inner child's intuition and wisdom.

8. I nurture and care for my inner child with compassion and tenderness.

9. I forgive myself for any mistakes or shortcomings and offer love to my inner child.

10. I reclaim my sense of wonder and curiosity, allowing my inner child to explore and learn.

11. I create a safe and nurturing environment for my inner child to thrive.

12. I celebrate and honor my inner child's unique qualities and gifts.

13. I release any shame or guilt associated with my inner child's needs and desires.

14. I reconnect with the playful and spontaneous nature of my inner child.

15. I give myself permission to rest and relax, honoring the need for balance in my life.

16. I embrace my creativity and allow my inner child to express it freely.

17. I am patient and gentle with myself as I heal and grow.

18. I give myself permission to have fun and enjoy life's simple pleasures.

19. I release any limiting beliefs that hold my inner child back from experiencing joy.

20. I am whole and complete, and I love every part of my inner child.

 **Dream Analysis**

Dream analysis can be a wonderful way to get to the core of what we are feeling and experiencing, how our emotions are processed, and more. Use the following to help you analyze your dreams by writing them down in a notebook alongside what you think their implications are:

- Playful activities in dreams reflect a longing for spontaneity, joy, and freedom.

- Childhood home or familiar places symbolize the need for security, comfort, or a sense of belonging.

- Interactions with your younger self or inner child indicate a need for healing, self-compassion, or rediscovering forgotten aspects of yourself.

- Parental figures or authority figures in dreams suggest unresolved issues or the need for guidance and support.

- Toys, games, or childhood objects symbolize nostalgia, innocence, or reconnecting with your playful nature.

- Fear or being scared as a child represents unresolved fears or anxieties resurfacing.

- Feeling lost or abandoned as a child indicates insecurity, loneliness, or a fear of lacking support.

- Positive interactions with your inner child symbolize self-care, self-love, and integrating past experiences.

- Witnessing or experiencing childhood trauma suggests the need for healing, therapy, or processing past events.

- School or educational settings represent a desire for knowledge, growth, or revisiting past lessons.

- Reuniting with childhood friends or loved ones symbolizes a longing for connection, support, or recapturing joy.

- Parental expectations or pressure from childhood indicate feeling overwhelmed, trapped, or the need to establish your identity.

- Being a child again symbolizes innocence, playfulness, and a need for nurturing.

- Childhood symbols (teddy bears, dolls) represent comfort, support, or a desire for companionship.

- Exploring nature or engaging in outdoor activities as a child symbolizes reconnecting with the natural world, finding peace, or embracing simplicity.

- Childhood memories hold insights or lessons to understand present patterns or behaviors.

- Unresolved conflicts or unfinished business from childhood suggest the need for resolution, closure, or forgiveness.

- Imaginary friends or fantastical creatures symbolize creativity, imagination, or inner resources and strengths.

- Being praised, rewarded, or achieving success as a child reflects a longing for recognition, validation, or revisiting feelings of accomplishment.

- Neglect or abuse as a child signals the need for healing, therapy, or acknowledging past wounds to move forward.

Now, you have some of the prerequisite skills required to help you along on your journey to heal your inner child. Whenever you find that you are feeling stressed, tense, zoned out, or otherwise in need of one of these exercises, feel free to return to them at any time in order to allow yourself to relax. In the next chapter, we'll explore something else crucial to your growth and healing of your inner child—cognitive behavioral therapy.

**EVERYTHING WE HEAR IS
AN OPINION, NOT A FACT.
EVERYTHING WE SEE IS A
PERSPECTIVE, NOT THE TRUTH.**

—MARCUS AURELIUS

Chapter 2

Cognitive Behavioral Therapy

COGNITIVE BEHAVIORAL THERAPY, also known as CBT, is one of the most common forms of therapy that is employed to allow us to heal. Together, let's uncover what CBT is and how it can help you along in this journey.

What Is CBT?

CBT is a method of psychotherapy, also referred to as talk therapy. This is because the primary component of the session—unlike in some forms of therapy—is discussion. During a CBT session, people learn to identify and change behaviors that have a negative influence on how they live their lives. For example, if someone has a common pattern of being self-deprecating with no explanation or logic behind those emotions, then their therapist will employ methods of CBT in order to teach them how these thoughts are destructive. This, then, enables a patient to think in a more constructive and realistic manner—one that drastically improves their quality of life overall.

In addition, we know CBT as one of the most widely researched forms of psychotherapeutic treatment. CBT wouldn't be around right now if it weren't effective. This is evidenced by the fact that we know CBT is effective in both the long and short term, allowing clients anywhere from temporary relief from a specified issue to long-term relief for a lifelong one. Additionally, CBT is used in the treatment of myriad different mental disorders, from depression to anxiety and more. In fact, some forms of CBT—such as dialectical behavior therapy—have been formulated to treat specific conditions like borderline personality disorder, but I digress.

Major Principles of CBT

Because CBT is both widely practiced and thoroughly developed, there are some major principles included in the concept that are important to understand. These principles describe the scope of treatment as well as the overarching goals of CBT. It is important to understand this, as these are factors that allow you to have realistic expectations for your practice—thus ensuring greater success.

Generally, there are nine principles that are included in CBT. The first principle involves thinking, which is why there was a strong emphasis on viewing thoughts as thoughts in the last chapter. This principle of CBT states that thinking plays a major role in how we process information as well as how that information impacts our emotions, motivation, and overall health. In other words, our thinking impacts how we perceive things and how we feel. This is why it is important to recognize that thoughts are thoughts as well as to improve thought processes that are unhealthy or harmful.

The next principle of CBT involves our distress. According to CBT, a significant amount of our distress is the direct result of maladaptive thinking. This means that CBT principles decree that harmful or illogical thinking patterns are one of the most significant contributors to our stress and upset. For example, maladaptive thinking patterns like cognitive distortions—which we will talk about shortly—involve thinking that is inherently flawed in some manner. Cognitive distortions play a significant role in our distress by making us feel like things are worse than they are or that we are less valuable than we truly are. As a result, we feel upset due to maladaptive thinking.

The third principle of CBT states that abnormal behavior is a result of errors in thinking. In other words, uncharacteristic behavior or behavior that exhibits traits of mental illness results from errors in the way that we think—meaning that those thoughts are illogical, flawed, or upsetting. For example, if you begin isolating yourself from social situations, then you are experiencing abnormal behavior as a result of thinking something negative and inaccurate—such as that no one likes you.

The fourth principle states that maladaptive thinking—thoughts that are flawed in some way—can be transformed into thoughts that are beneficial or productive. This means that your flawed thinking that makes you feel bad, behave strangely, or otherwise experience upset can be transformed into thinking that actually benefits you. How incredible!

The next principle of CBT involves automatic thoughts—ones that we think without even meaning to or having to force or that move by so quickly we do not even notice their existence. This principle states that everyone has these automatic thoughts but not everyone is able to recognize them. Being unable to recognize these thoughts can prove to be rather troublesome when it comes to inner child healing, as automatic thoughts do not represent our true intentions, yet a lack of recognition can make it seem like these thoughts are who we are.

Sixth is the principle that our automatic thoughts can eventually become habitual, which then impacts our emotions, motivations, and perceptions. This means that thoughts that happen so quickly we do not even notice them can have a significant impact on our lives—and that impact is usually negative. It seems like the solution to this would be learning to notice these automatic thoughts, which is one of the many skills that CBT therapists teach their clients.

Earlier, I mentioned that we would discuss cognitive distortions. How we perceive our reality isn't always accurate, which is a result of cognitive distortions. A cognitive distortion is a habitual thinking pattern that is intrinsically negative or inaccurate due to bias. Some examples of cognitive distortions include

- **overgeneralization**: This occurs when a general rule is made based on one event, and then that rule is applied to other situations. For example, if one time you threw up while eating cereal, you might overgeneralize that every time you eat cereal, you are going to throw up; therefore, you should never eat cereal again. In reality, this likely isn't the reason you threw up, nor is it a logical conclusion to come to.

- **arbitrary inference**: This involves coming to a specific conclusion without any evidence to back it up. For example, if someone says that red is their least favorite color, but it is your favorite, coming to the conclusion that that person must hate you is an arbitrary inference.

- **personalization**: Personalization involves thinking that an event is somehow related to you without there being any connection. For instance, if a stack of toilet paper falls over in the grocery store and you had no real impact on the matter, blaming yourself and stating that you shouldn't go outside is personalization.

- **polarized thinking:** This involves categorizing thoughts as one side of an extreme instead of recognizing that there are shades of gray in the world.

- **magnification and minimization:** This involves making something seem far bigger or smaller in importance than it truly is.

- **selective abstraction:** This involves taking a piece of information out of context selectively in order to avoid other information to come to a desired conclusion rather than being realistic.

Another principle of CBT states that sometimes, it is necessary to change the way that we see the world so that we can truly heal. This involves something called a cognitive schema, which refers to someone's perceptions of themselves, others, the world, the past and future, assumptions, beliefs, and more (Cherry, 2023). There are different cognitive schemas, including

- cognitive conceptual: the meaning of the world or core beliefs that you hold

- affective: feelings that are positive or negative

- physiological: how we perceive the physical world around us

- behavioral: actions we perform

- motivational: the desire to seek pleasure while simultaneously avoiding pain

The final principle of CBT is that our thoughts aren't always rational nor realistic. This can stem from something called systemic biases, which refers to how we process information in a way that can cause unhealthy responses. This can also cause misinterpretations, misconceptions, or other interpretations that are false or inaccurate.

Practical Applications of CBT

Now that you have a solid idea of not only what CBT is but what principles underlie it, it is time to uncover how CBT principles can be used to help you heal and grow as a person, both in and outside of inner child healing—specifically when it comes to trauma (the events that create a lasting negative impact on our lives). After all, trauma is one of the most significant reasons why inner child healing is necessary in the first place, which means that we need to delve into how CBT can be used in that regard.

CBT is one of the most effective methods of therapy when it comes to trauma, and there are many reasons for it. CBT is phenomenal for helping us challenge our thoughts—particularly unhealthy thought processes—that are connected to our trauma. In other words, if our trauma inspires us to think in a certain way, CBT is the best method for breaking this connection and allowing us to think in a way that is not dissimilar to how we thought before the trauma. In specific, CBT can help someone who is traumatized who had a healthy mindset go right back to the mindset that they had before, imbuing them with the confidence and frame of mind to continue moving forward in life. This can break down thoughts that directly connect to trauma and allow someone to recover much easier than if they didn't have CBT methods in their toolbox for recovery.

In addition, CBT requires that someone challenges their thought processes indiscriminately to determine which ones are unhealthy. It is hard work—work that not many people are up for at first. But at the end of the day, it is worthwhile work. This is because the challenge that CBT requires also allows for someone to face the reality of their trauma. When someone experiences trauma, one of the first things they are prone to thinking is that it wasn't that bad or that they can't have faced a traumatic experience. Being able to confront your trauma and recognize it for what it is is a massive step forward for your healing and in general.

Another one of the many practical applications of CBT is that it helps you gain emotional insight into your own life. Many people who face some form of trauma develop unconscious reactions to various circumstances in life—especially ones that serve as a reminder of one's trauma. As a result, someone can act in a way that isn't typical for them or that even harms them dramatically, all as a result of trauma. CBT forces people to explore their responses to these reminders of trauma, thus making it easier to dissolve these negative reactions to reminders of trauma—no matter what size they may be.

Furthermore, CBT can help reduce panic responses and their negative impacts. This is because CBT focuses on helping someone gain insight when it comes to their responses and emotions in life as well as how the two connect. Examining this connection can help reduce both the panic response one may feel as a result of trauma and the way that these panic responses manifest as impacts on one's daily life. Moreover, many patients who have experienced CBT notice marked improvements in their anxiety surrounding memories of trauma, making a compelling argument for the use of CBT in trauma recovery.

How Does CBT Connect to Inner Child Work?

All of these connections between trauma and CBT are excellent; they truly go to show how CBT can improve the life of someone who has experienced even the most severe trauma. But how does this connect to our topic at hand—to inner child work in specific? As it turns out, there are several ways that inner child work and CBT connect.

In a professional setting, for instance, a therapist can utilize what they learn in order to determine which responses are a result of a wounded inner child. In other words, not all of your responses are due to adulthood and your experiences thereof; rather, in some instances, your inner child has been harmed, usually in childhood itself. With the help of a professional, you can determine where your inner child's wounds stem from and what needs to be done in order to heal them.

However, we are not talking about going out and getting therapy only—we are talking about performing CBT methods on yourself in order to heal your inner child. That is what this workbook is all about. How can CBT help **you** alone heal your inner child? Using CBT methods, you can determine where your wounds stem from, including isolated events that harmed your inner child directly. This is how CBT can help you and what we'll explore moving forward.

In this chapter, you learned about how CBT works and what it is, the principles behind it, and how CBT can function connectively in helping with your healing process. In the next chapter, we'll focus on some tangible and actionable processes that allow you to apply CBT in real life.

Chapter 3

Cognitive Behavior Therapy Exercises

IN THE LAST CHAPTER, we talked all about what CBT is and how it applies to trauma and the process of healing. In this chapter, we are going to focus on the practical applications of that learning. Remember that if at any point you need to, you can return to the exercises from Chapter 1 to steady yourself. Keep your head up—you've got this.

If you have the intention to do so, you can take charge of how you think, feel, and act. This works because you can use awareness and CBT skills to practice doing so. Let's talk about how to do so now.

Exercise No. 1 **Relaxation Imagery**

In order to engage with this relaxing imagery exercise, I encourage you to find a spot where you are comfortable. You can be sitting down, lying down, or even standing up and walking around if that is most comfortable. Make sure that you won't have any outside interruptions for at least 10 minutes and that you are nice and comfortable with the temperature and volume level of the room.

I want you to begin in your relaxed state and start by focusing on your breath. Close your eyes if you feel comfortable doing so, or if you do not, just allow your gaze to soften on something in the room with you. I want you to envision that you are on a beautiful, clear beach. Visualize yourself sitting on that beach, letting the sand caress your skin and the sun—or lack thereof—gently kiss your body. How does the wind feel? Are there any birds in the sky? Dig your feet into the sand and let yourself feel the enveloping love of the ocean you sit before.

And speaking of the ocean, take a look at it. Pay attention to how the tides meet the sand, in and out just like your breathing. In and out, in and out. Watch the ocean swell on the horizon, and pay attention to the waves building up and crashing down. Breathe in time with the waves, feeling the gentle spray of the ocean on your face.

 Now, I want you to pay attention to the waves, but this time, I want you to visualize them as if they were your emotions. Imagine the swell of the waves is your pain, your frustration, your sadness rising higher and higher, and then collapsing as the waves crash. Keep watching the waves rise like your mounting emotions, and then watch as they crash. Time your breathing with the waves, imagining the waves filling your lungs, collecting up all of those negative emotions—in, in, in! When your lungs are full, visualize the waves crashing as you release those negative emotions.

Breathe in and out, in and out, allowing yourself to settle into this new feeling of calm and relaxation. This is your beach now, your ocean with your tides. Whenever you feel yourself returning to feelings of instability, whether it be anger, sadness, or some other form of frustration, take a moment to steady your tides, remembering how positive and peaceful you feel in this moment. Remember that you are the one in control and that you can keep yourself calm with exercises like this one.

As we close out this relaxing imagery exercise, slowly bring your awareness back to the present and back to your body. Wiggle your fingers and toes, allowing yourself to come back to the room you are in, and open your eyes if you've closed them. How do you feel? After an activity like this, I always feel far more relaxed and at ease, and I hope you do too. Even if you still feel tense, I am proud of you for trying and working toward bettering yourself. You are doing great, even if you do not recognize that right now.

Exercise No. 2 **Noticing Thoughts**

The next exercise that I want to take you through involves noticing your thoughts. Simply put, this exercise is aimed at helping you become aware of your thoughts. Learning to notice and identify when we are engaging with automatic thoughts is an important aspect of recovery since these automatic thoughts can influence us greatly.

Thought records are a trace of what we think, including our automatic thoughts. Thought records are helpful because they expose negative thoughts to the light of day, allowing us to know not just that we have these negative thoughts but what they are as well (Psychology Tools, n.d.). Thought records are also useful in helping us identify problems with our thinking as well as for allowing us to challenge our negative thoughts and change our patterns of thinking for the better.

In order to keep a thought record, you have to start paying attention to the thoughts that you are having—especially when it comes to moments where your feelings seem to be shifting. To help you along, here are the steps in completing one:

1. Record information regarding the situation in which you noticed this emotional change. In addition, make sure to write down anybody you were with. Finally for the situation, record in as much detail as you can anything that is happening right before you felt the shift in your mood, no matter how trivial it may seem.

2. Next is the emotional aspect. You are going to need to describe your emotions as well as any physical sensations involved in this shift. Think about what emotional shift prompted you to begin recording as well as any accompanying physical feelings. Then, try to describe your emotion in one word, as most emotions can be—such as "anger" or "sadness." Once you've selected a word, rate the strength of the emotion based on the percentage of it you felt. Then, record what sensations you felt in your body. Finally, you are going to record the thoughts that came through your mind in this instance.

Once you have your thought record written out, it is important that you actually take some time to analyze it. See if you can highlight any consistencies within it. For example, you may notice that certain behavioral shifts occur often in the same places or around the same people. This is a clear indicator that these locations or individuals may be triggering for you, for instance. Noticing these commonalities is a fantastic way to identify triggers for shifts in your behavior or thought patterns.

Overall, keeping a thought record is a skillful way to notice your thinking patterns and evaluate them, keeping track of how your thoughts influence your mood and behavior shifts as well as what circumstances alter the ways in which you think.

Exercise No. 3 Noticing Thinking Habits

This activity builds off of the last one. If you didn't work on a thought record in accordance with the last activity, I definitely recommend going back and doing one so that you can get the most out of this activity. This activity is focused on guiding you through your thought record in a bit more detail, allowing you to identify any maladaptive thought patterns that are impacting your life significantly.

Each of the following 10 questions is geared toward helping you identify maladaptive thought patterns. I recommend using them to guide you through an analysis of your thought record in order to see where these flaws in thinking occur. Your questions are as follows:

1. **Does the thought you've identified in your thought record discount the positive by magnifying the negative?** In other words, does this thought exclude the positive aspects of a situation in favor of the negative aspects of the situation?

2. **Is the particular thought that you are analyzing one that takes the perspective of an extreme?** In other words, is this a thought that negates the shades of gray involved in a scenario?

3. **Are you making any assumptions when it comes to this thought or line of thinking?** In other words, are you making an assumption in your thinking that tries to predict the future or read the mind of someone else? What evidence is there to support your assumption?

4. **Is this thought one that anticipates the worst case scenario or something generally terrible happening?** In other words, are you expecting the worst to happen or something really bad to happen as a result of a situation?

5. **Is this thought one that stems from a compulsive need to be right all of the time?** In other words, did you think this thought because you feel like you have to prove yourself or be correct in a situation?

6. **Is the thought you had one that stems from a resistance to change?** In other words, is this thought one that is the result of a desire to keep things exactly as they were?

7. **Is this thought one that pertains to you feeling as though something simply isn't fair?** In other words, did your thought have to do with a sense of fairness you feel you should've received, yet others do not agree with it or see it the same way?

8. **Is this thought in conjunction with blaming someone else for something that happened to you or something you felt?** In other words, do you feel like someone else is responsible for your pain or what's going on in your life?

9. **Is your thought a "should" thought?** In other words, does it involve the belief that something should have happened a certain way or that someone should've behaved a certain way? Why do you think you held this belief in this moment?

10. Finally, **does your thought have to do with believing that because you feel it, it must be true?** In other words, do you feel like just because you had an emotion that means it is the reality of a situation?

Now that you've had some time to explore these questions with your thought record, see if you notice any pattern regarding the kinds of thoughts that lead to maladaptive thinking. Furthermore, try to brainstorm any potential solutions to these thought processes, jotting down how you can overcome them.

Exercise No. 4 **Think Negative**

Thinking negatively is the exact thing that we are trying to avoid; however, thinking negative thoughts with a degree of intention can actually be helpful. This exercise is geared toward helping you recognize your life scripts—negative thoughts that pop up over and over, almost on cue when certain things happen.

For example, think of something mean you've said to yourself today. Is it something you usually say to yourself? If so, that is an instance of a life script. By overcoming your life scripts, you can overcome negativity—but first, you have to actually be able to recognize them. Some other examples of life scripts include

- I'll never be good enough.
- I am just like my mother/father.
- I never do anything right.

Notice how all of these thoughts revolve around something negative that is also an extreme, black-and-white thought.

In order to help you overcome your life scripts, you have to first recognize what they are—what those thoughts that you repeat to yourself really are and why they are there in the first place. This is going to require you to step out of your comfort zone a bit. To help you, I am going to provide you with some common, triggering scenarios that provoke most people to think of a negative life script.

Triggering Life Scripts

As mentioned, we are going to start with some situations that typically trigger negative lift scripts. For each of the scenarios below, envision yourself in the situation and then write down the most negative thing you could say to yourself in that scenario in the space below.

- **being rejected**: If you are in a relationship, imagine your partner breaks up with you and the feeling is not mutual. It comes on rather suddenly, and you have no way to anticipate the situation. What would you say to yourself? If you are not in a relationship, imagine the person that you like the most, someone you surely thought would say yes, says no to you asking to make things official. What would you say to yourself in this situation?

- **unfair treatment**: Imagine you are at work, and you and a coworker do the exact same thing. The boss doesn't like it and sees you both doing it. However, your boss only gets mad at you for it, publicly reprimanding you while ignoring your coworker's involvement—or worse, commending them for how they handled the situation. What is the worst thing that you could say to yourself at this moment?

- **disagreement in beliefs**: Imagine that your friend, someone who you respect highly, has a political or religious belief that differs drastically from your own. They are not willing to back down and even go as far as saying something offensive about your own belief in a fit of rage. What is the worst thing you'd be thinking to yourself right now?

- **someone in your friend group speaks over you**: They do not apologize or even acknowledge that you were speaking, instead opting to continue on with whatever it was that they were saying. No one else speaks up for you either. How are you feeling, and what would you say to yourself?

_____
_____
_____
_____
_____
_____
_____
_____
_____
_____
_____
_____
_____
_____
_____
_____
_____
_____
_____
_____
_____

Processing Your Life Scripts

After completing that portion of the activity, it is time to process your responses. Remember what we did in Chapter 1 to process the results of each activity? We answered some questions. Similarly, we are going to answer some here as well. Answer the following in the space below:

- Which of these thoughts were the most common for you, ones you think to yourself on a daily or regular basis?

- Are these thoughts things that someone has told you, either directly or indirectly, about yourself?

- How many times would you estimate that you engage with a negative life script per day?

- If your best friend, child, or sibling were in the same situation, would you tell them the things that you tell yourself? If not, write down what you would tell a friend in the same situation.

My hope is that processing these answers will help you realize something; not everything you say to yourself is fair nor rational. While we tend to believe these cruel things when they are said within our own minds, they are not true at all if said to someone else—they are simply mean.

Understanding that your negative life scripts are nothing more than mean, conditioned comments that you wouldn't really say to someone else is a valuable step forward. Not only does this help you realize that just because you feel something doesn't mean it is true, but it helps you understand that it is not okay to  be unkind to yourself simply because those thoughts are private— because really, they are only doing you a disservice.

If you notice yourself thinking a thought that you recognize as a negative life script, simply ask yourself what you'd tell a friend in the same scenario. You should treat yourself like your own best friend, and slowly you will begin to flip those negative life scripts on their head.

Exercise No. 5 Validating Assumptions

When we experience strong emotions, it can cause us to make various assumptions about the world around us, other people, and the future. Just because you feel something doesn't mean it is an accurate representation of what's going on in the real world or how others feel about you. Feeling like the world is ending and the world *actually* ending are two different things. Something that can be massively beneficial is learning how to test the validity of various assumptions in order to determine what is true and what simply proves to be an inconsistency or distortion of thought.

I am going to provide you with five statements. I want you to read these statements and think about them for a moment, considering the implications of each statement and what kind of mood someone must be in to be thinking this way:

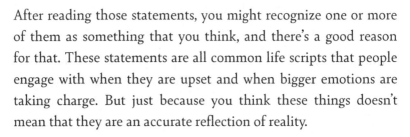

1. Everyone hates me.

2. I am never going to be successful.

3. I am not good at anything.

4. There's nothing that can make me feel better.

5. The world isn't meant for me.

After reading those statements, you might recognize one or more of them as something that you think, and there's a good reason for that. These statements are all common life scripts that people engage with when they are upset and when bigger emotions are taking charge. But just because you think these things doesn't mean that they are an accurate reflection of reality.

So what is there to do? In order to overcome this, there is a simple solution: you have to test the validity of your cognitions—or, in other words, determine how realistic your thoughts are. You can do so with the following steps:

1. Consider the situation at hand. Define it and name it—what's going on?

2. Gather information that proves the statement or situation wrong.

3. Gather information that proves the situation to be correct.

   a. Take the information that proves the situation to be correct and determine if it is valid based on whether or not it makes an assumption or falls into another cognitive distortion.

4. Find outside confirmation that the statement is true, such as from a friend, family member, or professional, in order to confirm that the statement exists outside of yourself.

Take those steps and try to apply them yourself by using one of the five statements above. To show you what I mean, here is how to work through the statement that "everyone hates me":

Statement:	1. Everyone hates me.
Evidence to the contrary:	1. My friend told me that she likes me and values our friendship just yesterday. 2. I was invited out to brunch next week; if my friends did not like me, they wouldn't invite me out. 3. My cat loves me. 4. My sister loves me. 5. My partner loves me.
Evidence to support:	1. My friend interrupted me at lunch today and I never got to finish what I was saying. **Is this based on a cognitive distortion or assumption?** 1. Yes—it assumes that they meant to and that interrupting me leads to hatred.
Can an authority confirm validity?	No; therefore, the statement is incorrect.

Repeat this method with one or more of the statements above, even grabbing some paper to carry a hard copy of this chart with you in the event that you need to check the validity of a thought in the future.

This is one of my favorite CBT-based exercises because it is so effective and has many benefits. It can, for example, demonstrate a few things to us:

1. Our thoughts can *sound* rather correct, even if they are not correct. This can include faulty assumptions and is a valuable aspect of this exercise because it shows us that 1) it is normal to assume the way we do and 2) these incorrect assumptions do not have as much power as we give them initially.

2. Just because something seems to make sense, it doesn't mean it is logical. Even if our thoughts seem to be reasonable to us, it doesn't mean that they are. As demonstrated in the chart, it is easy to think everyone hates you, but when you break the evidence down, you prove to yourself quite the contrary— plenty of people do like you.

3. "Always" or "never" can often serve as clues to indicate that someone is engaging in overgeneralization.

After finishing this activity, I hope you will take a few moments to reflect on what you've learned and gained before moving onto the next one.

Exercise No. 6 Reframing Cognitive Distortions

As the title suggests, this activity is geared toward helping you reframe cognitive distortions. We talked about them in detail earlier—how cognitive distortions are intrinsically flawed ways of thinking—but we didn't really go into how we could circumvent them step-by-step. Using something called Beck's ABC model, we'll learn to overcome cognitive distortions together.

Beck's ABC model is often used within CBT-related circles. It is a multi-step guide that shows how certain events cause our behaviors and how lines of thought typically unfold. Regardless, the model goes like this (The Decision Lab, 2023):

A. **Activating event**: The activating event is something that happens either to you directly or around you, meaning that an activating event can simply be witnessed. This is the first step in having a thought; something has to trigger that thought.

B. **Belief**: As a result of the activating event, a belief is formed. This is the initial thought that you have, which can be either rational or irrational. For example, a child touching a hot stove (activating event) would develop the rational belief that touching the stove is going to cause them to get burned, which is undesirable.

C. **Consequence**: As a result of a belief that was formed—which again can be irrational or rational—a consequence takes place. If the belief was rational, then a healthy consequence will occur; however, if the belief was irrational, then an unhealthy consequence will occur.

D. **Disputation**: This occurs when someone experiences an unhealthy consequence as a result of an irrational belief. In order to avoid unhealthy consequences, one must dispute their belief to transform it into one that is rational.

E. **New effect**: This is the final step in the process. It occurs when someone transforms an irrational belief into a rational one, thus creating a healthier consequence.

You might be wondering how this can help you. The benefit of the ABC model lies in the first three steps—the A, B, and C. In order to overcome cognitive distortions via reframing, you have to analyze not just what the distortion is but where it stems from. Using the space below, try to work out the A, B, and C of a current cognitive distortion that you are experiencing.

Based on the undesirable consequences that inevitably occur as a result of an irrational belief, adapt your belief to be different—even if you have to adopt a "fake it 'til you make it" frame of mind.

After you work toward shifting your belief, analyze how your consequences have changed. Do you notice an improved consequence as a result of shifting your mindset to a more rational one? Of course you do! That is the power of the ABC model.

Exercise No. 7 **Exploring Cognitive Schemas**

Next up, we are going to work on exploring cognitive schemas. We've already talked about what these are, which is why this activity is going to be so heavily question-based. Using the space provided, answer each of the following sets of questions revolving around your thoughts, feelings, and beliefs in order to explore your cognitive schemas.

- *on the self*

  ☐ How do you perceive yourself?

  ☐ If you had to describe yourself in three words, which three words would you select and why?

  ☐ How do you feel your friends perceive you? What about any family members you have? How about your coworkers? Why do you feel they have these perceptions of you?

  ☐ What is your favorite quality about yourself and why? What about your least favorite?

  ☐ What is one thing that you think you do better than anyone else?

_____

_____

_____

_____

_____

_____

_____

_____

_____

_____

_____

_____

- *on others*

  ☐ Who is your best friend? What are some qualities that you admire about them?

  ☐ What are some qualities that you look for in friends?

  ☐ How can you tell if someone likes or dislikes you? How can you tell if you like or dislike someone else?

  ☐ What do you notice about others the most in regard to personality **and** appearance?

  ☐ What intrinsically draws you to someone or makes you feel connected to them.

_____

_____

_____

_____

_____

_____

_____

_____

_____

_____

_____

_____

_____

- *on the world*

  ☐ What is your favorite thing about the world? What about your least favorite thing?

  ☐ Do you believe the world is a good or bad place? Why?

  ☐ Is the world generally somewhere you consider to be safe, dangerous, or somewhere in the middle? Why?

  ☐ What do you define as "the world"?

  ☐ If you could change anything in the world, what would it be and why?

- *on the past*

    ☐ What is your general opinion of your past? How would you describe it in one word?

    ☐ What is your favorite part of your past? What about your least favorite?

    ☐ If you could change anything about your past, what would it be and why?

    ☐ Would you willingly relive your past for any reason?

    ☐ Do you believe that your past has been valuable to you in some way? Why?

- *on the present*

  ☐ How do you generally perceive your current set of circumstances in life?

  ☐ What would you change about your present situation, and why?

  ☐ Do you believe that your present set of circumstances are fair to you or that they are particularly unfair?

  ☐ What would make your present situation better or more favorable for you, and why?

  ☐ Is there anything in your present that you are particularly grateful for?

● *on the future*

☐ Generally speaking, do you believe that your future will be more positive or more negative than your past? What about the present?

☐ What do you think your future is going to be like?

☐ What are your goals? Do these align with your idea of what the future will be like?

☐ What is something someone always told you would happen in your future? Do you actually see that happening?

☐ What is something you hope your future contains but you are not sure of?

- **on your goals**

  ☐ What are some of your long-term goals right now? What about short-term goals?

  ☐ What is a goal you thought you would achieve but haven't been able to? How does that make you feel?

  ☐ What's something you never thought you'd be able to achieve but you have achieved? How does that make you feel?

  ☐ What is a goal that someone else has that makes you feel any strong emotion? What emotion and why?

  ☐ Is there a goal you feel like you should have but do not? Why do you feel like you should have that goal?

_____

_____

_____

_____

_____

_____

_____

_____

_____

_____

_____

- *on your memories*

  ☐ What is a particularly "good" memory that you have? Why do you consider it to be a good memory?

  ☐ What's a particularly "bad" memory that you have? Why do you think of it that way?

  ☐ How do you perceive the quality of your memory to be?

  ☐ What is something you are not sure happened, but you have a memory of it anyway?

  ☐ What is something that you remember, but it doesn't seem like anyone else does?

● *on your expectations*

- [ ] What is something you expect that frequently isn't met?

- [ ] What is an expectation that you feel is being or has been forced upon you? Does this align with your own expectations of yourself?

- [ ] Do you perceive your expectations of yourself to be gentle or harsh? Why?

- [ ] What do you expect of other people, and why?

- [ ] Do you think expectations can be positive and negative? Why or why not?

_____

_____

_____

_____

_____

_____

_____

_____

_____

_____

_____

_____

_____

- *on right and wrong*

  ☐ Do you believe that right and wrong can easily be defined?

  ☐ What do you think makes something right? What about wrong?

  ☐ Do you perceive your actions to be more right or more wrong?

  ☐ Do you perceive the actions of others to be more right or more wrong?

  ☐ What is the line between right and wrong?

  ☐ on your current physical condition

  ☐ What would you describe as constituting your current physical condition?

  ☐ Describe your current physical condition. How do you feel about it?

  ☐ What are your beliefs about your physical condition?

  ☐ Do you compare your physical condition to that of others? If so, what do you compare and why?

  ☐ What do you believe makes someone have a good physical condition?

● *on past and current actions*

☐ Do you believe you can justify your past actions? What about your current ones?

☐ How has your behavior in the past made you feel?

☐ Are you proud of your current self and its actions?

☐ Do you believe that your past or current behaviors are a result of someone else's teachings?

☐ Do you feel like you could serve as a role model to others?

After you've answered as many questions as you can, simply move on to the next activity.

Exercise No. 8 Seeing a New Way

Congrats! You've made it to the final activity of the chapter! In this activity, we are going to use the answers you devised from the last one. So, if you skipped Exercise 7, I recommend going back to it now. For this exercise, use the space below to summarize your beliefs and group them in accordance with whether they make you feel positive, negative, or neutral. Then, look at the ones that make you feel positive and negative—because a faulty schema is faulty whether it makes us feel good or bad—and use the resources from Exercise 6 to modify those schemas.

In this chapter, you were introduced to eight excellent exercises to help you employ cognitive behavioral therapy methods for your healing. How delightful! In the next chapter, we are going to focus on journaling and working with every single part of ourselves for maximum effect. Trust me, you won't want to miss it.

NEUROSCIENCE RESEARCH
SHOWS THAT THE ONLY WAY
WE CAN CHANGE THE WAY WE
FEEL IS BY BECOMING AWARE
OF OUR INNER EXPERIENCE AND
LEARNING TO BEFRIEND WHAT IS
GOING INSIDE OURSELVES.

–BESSEL A. VAN DER KOLK

Chapter 4

Journaling and Parts Work

IT MIGHT BE TEMPTING to skip this chapter for some people, especially those who underestimate the power of journaling. But this chapter is possibly one of the most effective, and I recommend sticking around until the end. In this chapter, you will learn to employ something called internal family systems (IFS) therapy alongside journaling in order to heal your inner child. It is a method that is well-researched and effective, yet not many people know of it. Let's explore what IFS is and how it can help you together.

IFS: A Sophisticated Approach to Healing Your Inner Child

Internal family systems (IFS) refers to a therapeutic method that is based on a model first created by Richard Schwartz (IFS Institute, n.d.-b). Contrary to the name, IFS has nothing to do with family therapy or even other people; rather, IFS is internally focused on you and you alone. In IFS, a patient will explore their subpersonalities, which are known as "parts" within the scope of IFS. These parts include various components that build up and represent us as a whole. Not only do parts in IFS include your inner child and the parts that make it up, but it also includes a variety of other parts. Each part of you, according to IFS, has its own feelings, perspectives, and motivations, which is why, at times, we can feel very conflicted.

The Fundamental Principles of IFS

The fortunate news about this concept is that IFS isn't very hard to understand. The sole fundamental principle of IFS is that we all have parts within ourselves, often referred to as "subpersonalities." Each of these little personalities is like a little person that resides within you. Imagine being made up of several different people, all with different goals and motivations. This is how IFS argues the human mind is composed. It's also important to note that this differs from the diagnosis of dissociative identity disorder; one is a disorder that causes difficulties in living and must be identified by a professional, whereas the IFS principle of parts is a natural state of being. Each part is going to have a different maturity level, attitude, personality, level of intelligence and wisdom—because yes, they differ—and tolerance to pain. What traumatizes one part might be a walk in the park for another, and vice versa. Each part is something fundamentally different within you, and in order to heal, IFS argues that each part should be worked with and treated as a distinct part that makes up the whole of you (The Self).

The Self

IFS therapy has very clear ideas of what is defined as the Self. The Self is, well, yourself. It is everything that makes you up and your consciousness, your will and motivations, and more. According to the principles of IFS, people are whole when this collection of parts that make them up come together. The Self is the true self or center of these parts, which can distinguish who you are from distinct parts. In other words, imagine that you have a part represented by your inner child, another represented by your anger, and one represented by kindness. This is a very watered-down version of what IFS states, but if you can imagine yourself like this, then you can imagine the Self—the cumulative whole of all of these parts.

The reason that we behave in ways that are maladaptive can, according to IFS, be explained relatively simply. Instead of tuning in to the Self, someone who allows their parts to take control will behave in a way that is cognitively distorted based on trauma, past experiences, and more. However, there's some good news—even people who are dominated by their parts can access the Self. This means that anyone can access the Self and its associated positive qualities of compassion, calm, curiosity, and wisdom. Accessing the Self is the best way to feel connected to the world around you and at peace.

The Parts

So far, it might seem like the parts are all bad, but that is not true. Parts can have extreme roles, which are unhealthy. This is because health and stability are found in balance. But the parts can also have healthy roles that benefit us overall. In general, there are three extreme roles that parts will take on, usually after they've experienced some form of trauma. In other words, extreme roles are only held by parts after experiencing some form of trauma that has deeply impacted you in some way. Note that this doesn't necessarily mean that the trauma had to be severe—just that it impacted you in some deep way.

Like I said, there are three roles that parts can take on when it comes to extremes. The first role is the manager role. As the name suggests, manager parts try to take on the role of preemptively protecting us from harm. This can occur after trauma or a close brush with it, as a manager part is going to try and prevent further pain from occurring. This might not sound like a bad thing, but it can actually hold you back significantly. This is because manager parts are perfectionists; any failure reflects on them significantly. What's more is that managers can't identify the difference between a good risk and a bad risk—meaning that all risks are negated to protect you. This can keep you from growing as a person, experiencing new things, and healing from past traumas as well as present ones.

The next part is exiles. Exiles are parts that experience pain, shame, fear, or trauma, and they are usually representative of inner child wounds. They are called exiles because managers and firefighters—the third of the extremes—try to force these parts out of the consciousness. In other words, part of you tries to forget or "exile" these inner child wounds so that they cannot come to the surface. The brain thinks this is a good method for keeping you safe, but when it comes down to it, avoiding the pain is only negative. It buries pain instead of confronting it, which is the easier option but not the most effective one.

The third and final of the extreme parts are firefighters. These parts exist to suppress exiles when they reach out and demand attention. This is why it is often really hard to confront our childhood trauma; there is a part dedicated to preventing us from doing so.

Ultimately, the goal of IFS is to help restore extreme and/or wounded parts of us in order to establish a healthy and harmonious inner system that is guided by the Self.

Steps of the IFS Process

In general, the IFS process is as follows (Rizzo, 2021):

1. **Find**: Identify the unique parts of yourself.

2. **Focus**: Pay special attention to each of the parts that you were able to identify.

3. **Flesh Out**: Describe each part in as much detail as possible.

4. **Feel Toward**: Determine which emotions are felt toward each of the parts you were able to identify.

5. **Befriend**: Learn to accept each of the parts without judgment and recognize the seemingly vital role they played in preserving the Self as well as that they are valuable regardless of whether their protection was effective.

6. **Unburden**: Help the parts shed their extreme roles and trust the Self to do what it does best—lead you.

How Does IFS Connect to Inner Child Work?

A few decades ago, inner child work was a concept that began to reach social consciousness. More and more people began to talk about healing the inner child, which was at the time a very innovative concept that allowed people to work toward healing the wounds of the inner child. However, over time, the IFS system began to become the predominant method of healing inner child wounds, as it is a well-researched and sound psychotherapeutic practice.

Why did we move to IFS in the first place? Well, the older approaches were effective but not as effective as they could be. This is because the older approaches assumed that it was easy to access the inner child, trauma wouldn't arise when doing so, it was easy to determine what the inner child needs, and that you love your inner child. As you can probably tell, with ease, in fact, most of these statements aren't going to be true for anyone with severe inner child wounds. This is why it was necessary to support inner child healing with the researched methods of IFS. It is able to address some of these concerns because

- IFS recognizes that there are different parts of ourselves that can make it hard to access the inner child because specific parts keep the inner child locked away. IFS methods are able to access and befriend these parts so that we can break into the inner child.

- IFS recognizes that because the inner child carries so much pain, you can feel that pain all over again even to the point of harm when trying to heal the inner child. IFS methods help ground you in the Self so that pain is productive and not dangerous to your healing.

- IFS recognizes that you can't just give your inner child messages; you have to actually feel the messages for the healing to happen. Your inner child has to actually take them in, which is something that IFS can ensure.

In summary, IFS has become the predominant method of inner child healing because of how it addresses the parts that make us up.

Finding an IFS Therapist Near You

I mentioned briefly earlier on that it may be a good idea to seek out a certified IFS therapist when it comes to working through your parts and coming to align with your true Self. You can do so by checking out www.ifs-institute.com/practitioners or www.seekdeeply.com.

IFS Techniques to Kickstart Your Way to Healing

This section focuses on the activities that you can engage with in order to contain your parts and work toward accessing your inner child. Because of this, it is very important that you follow each exercise in order for the maximum benefit.

Exercise No. 1 **How to Ground Yourself**

Grounding yourself is a very important part of the process. During this exercise, parts may try to overtake you or you may feel such strong emotions that you are not sure how to handle them. By grounding, you preemptively ensure that this won't happen. One of my favorite grounding exercises goes like this (Schwarts, 2021):

1. Close your eyes and take a few deep breaths. Make sure your feet are planted firmly on the floor.

2. Envision yourself as a tree. Imagine roots sprouting from the bottoms of your feet and extending into the earth, keeping you solid and steady.

3. Stretch your arms—your branches—up above your head, feeling the sturdiness of the entire "trunk" of your body.

And that is it! It doesn't seem like much, but it is a spectacularly effective exercise.

Exercise No. 2 **Getting to Know Your Parts**

In this exercise, you will learn how to identify and distinguish the different parts that make you up using something called a parts mapping technique. Go through the steps of the exercise carefully in order to determine and identify your parts, as well as ground yourself further. This step is important because it lays the foundation for ensuring that your inner child's wounds do not impact you in a negative way later on.

The steps for this exercise are as follows (Schwartz, 2021):

1. Focus your intention internally. You are going to want to talk to yourself for this activity, which you can do either in your head or aloud depending on your comfort level. Take a few deep, calming breaths and then focus inward. Tell yourself that you want to help anyone who needs it, but you have to know them in order to help. This serves as an initial call for the parts to come forward if they need help and are willing to accept it.

2. Next, you are going to tell yourself and your parts that if they overwhelm you, you can't help them. This will let your parts know that you are unable to help if they overwhelm you, bring forward something excessive, or try to take control.

3. Request that your parts work with you instead of taking you over. Tell them that when they are ready, let you know who they are and you will write it down. Because of this, you are going to need a piece of paper on which to record what comes forward.

4. This next step can be a bit confusing for some people. To some, the parts truly seem to talk back, while for others the parts simply embody you for a moment. In order to record each of the parts so that you have their identities, record any thoughts, emotions, or feelings that arise during your experience, until nothing new comes forward.

Once you've done this, you should have a sound idea of who each part is and what their purpose or predominant emotional tie to you is.

Exercise No. 3 **Getting to Know Your Protectors**

In this activity, we are going to help you get to know the protective parts of you. This is an important part of the process because, as I mentioned earlier, the protective parts are going to keep your inner child under lock and key. In order to access your inner child, you first have to gain the trust of your protector parts. The steps to do so are as follows (Schwartz, 2021):

1. Consider the protective parts of your personality. Where in your body do you feel their presence? You might feel tension, a temperature change, or something else that indicates their presence. Focus inwardly on this part.

2. If you could imagine what this part looks like, what do you think their appearance would be? How do you think their voice would sound? Can you imagine them engaging in any particular actions? Record anything that makes them unique.

3. Try to describe in as much detail as possible how you feel about this part. Sometimes other parts can interject with their opinions, but you should try to let the Self have the most influence over this. Remember that your Self is kind, compassionate, and curious, meaning that any malicious or hatred infused thoughts are stemming from another part. You can identify whether a thought comes from the Self based on if it is calm, clear, and confident; otherwise, it may be the words of another part. Ask the part speaking up to step aside, and let them know that their turn will come up soon. Keep trying until you get to the core of your Self to form an opinion about your protectors.

4. Befriend the part you are interacting with. Ask them how they got this role, what their ideal role would be, how old they are, and what they would like you to know about them.

5. Finally, find out what this part is afraid of, especially in the context of them not being around to do their job.

Repeat this process with every part that needs it.

After you've finished those activities, it is important to understand how you can befriend your parts—and the exiles especially. Doing so can prove to be a bit challenging. Think about it in the context of a real-life friendship with a person who doesn't exist inside of you. It can be rather tricky to befriend someone if you are doing so with an ulterior motive. So rather than taking this approach to the situation, befriend them openly and honestly as you would anyone else. Truly take your time on this stage. The best way to move forward with your self-led IFS journey so that you can befriend your parts is through journaling, which we will discuss in a later section.

Other IFS Exercises

To help guide you along with your IFS journey, here are a few more activities!

The Six Fs

A common exercise in IFS circles, the six Fs exercise is geared toward helping you identify each part of yourself. Fill out the chart!

Find the part: Where do you feel this part within your body? When you think about this part, does anything notable come to mind?	
Focus: Focus on that particular element and see if anything comes up. Write it down.	
Flesh it out: Is there anything notable about that part? How far from you is it? Is there anything you notice it thinking or saying? How old would you say this part is?	
Feel: How do you feel about this part? Use the Eight Cs activity below to help you.	
Befriend: What would you like this part to know? What is its role? Communicate with that part of you.	
Fear: What is that part afraid will happen if it is not there to do its job?	

The Eight Cs

Another common IFS exercise is the eight Cs exercise. This activity is going to help you rank the intensity of feelings you feel in a given moment. On a scale of 1–10, rate each of the following:

- curiosity:
- compassion:
- connectedness:
- clarity:
- creativity:
- confidence:
- courage:
- calm:

A Gift

If you could give your inner child a gift, what would it be? Draw or create a representation of that gift and explain its significance in helping your inner child heal.

Journaling as a Valuable Tool

Journaling is the best thing that you can do to help you get to know all of your parts. You need to keep a journal if you hope to truly befriend the parts that reside within you. You can do so with a containment ritual that uses something called hash writing.

Hash Writing

The first part of hash writing—a method known to reduce stress and provide succinct clarity into mental health connections—involves setting up a containment ritual, which is an IFS tactic to  keep a pattern of behaviors associated with your therapeutic work (Aaron-Wayne, 2022). The purpose of a containment ritual is to ensure that the work you do is contained, or separated from your daily experience. In order to set up a containment ritual, you are going to need a journal, something to write with, and a ritual object. Your ritual object is going to be something that matters to you that can be moved in front of and away from you as you progress through the ritual. This helps act as a mental cue that the ritual is going and is over, allowing your brain to compartmentalize well.

The first step is selecting something to be used as a ritual object. It can be anything you want so long as it matters to you. Next, you are going to choose something that signals entering and leaving your inner space. Most people opt for a phrase, poem, or prayer, but you can use a phrase like "I am now entering/leaving my inner space" if none of those resonate with you. The most important part is consistency. The final part for setting up is choosing a distinct motion—like a hand gesture, pose, or movement—that indicates leaving or entering your inner space.

Before you begin your writing and exploration ritual, you need to perform your containment ritual. Place the object in front of you first, keeping your eyes on it as you steady your breathing. Then, speak or think your phrase loud and clearly, and then engage with your movement. Once you've done that, you can begin with the writing phase.

Before you begin writing, you are going to want to set a timer for about 10–15 minutes. You can absolutely set your timer for longer if you feel like you will need more time. Once that is set up, you can begin working with the following steps (Aaron-Wayne, 2022):

1. Pay attention to what you are feeling in the present moment. If your body feels tense, a thought or image enters your mind, or anything else comes up, focus on it and write it down. Be honest and earnest, writing down whatever arises.

2. As you write, pay attention to the tone or pattern of thoughts. Every time you perceive a shift happening—which would represent another part speaking—leave a line or two of space between what you are recording.

3. Continue writing until the timer runs out, allowing yourself to follow the last few steps closely without paying attention to how much time is left. Just keep writing.

4. After the timer goes off, give the thoughts about five minutes to settle. This allows your parts to wrap up any conversations that they may be having or finish any disagreements.

5. Once that timer is up, thank your parts for speaking and allow them to relax as you get ready to exit your inner space.

6. Finally, you are going to perform your containment ritual in the reverse order, moving, then speaking, then moving the object. If you need to ground yourself, using Exercise 1 from this chapter will help you.

You should notice that, over time, as you repeat this exercise, you get closer to your parts and they get closer to one another. You'll learn that they all have distinct identities, feelings, and motivations, and fighting may dissipate into the background.

Journaling Prompts for Inner Child Healing

Work with one or more of the following CBT-based journaling prompts for inner child healing:

1. Reflect on a specific childhood experience that still impacts you today. What thoughts and beliefs about yourself or the world did you develop as a result of that experience? How can you challenge and reframe those beliefs now?

2. Write a letter to your younger self, offering words of love, compassion, and encouragement. What advice or support would you give them?

3. Identify a negative or critical inner voice that often arises. Write down the specific thoughts it brings up. Then, challenge those thoughts by providing evidence that disproves them or offers a more balanced perspective.

4. Recall a moment of joy or happiness from your childhood. Describe the memory in detail and explore how you can reconnect with that sense of joy in your present life.

5. List three qualities or strengths that your inner child possesses. How can you integrate those qualities into your adult life to enhance your well-being and self-expression?

6. Think about a time when you felt rejected or abandoned as a child. How does that experience impact your relationships or fears of rejection as an adult? Explore ways to cultivate self-acceptance and build healthy connections with others.

7. Identify a limiting belief about yourself that was formed during your childhood. Challenge this belief by listing evidence that supports a more positive and empowering perspective.

8. Recall a favorite childhood activity or hobby. How can you incorporate elements of that activity into your current life to promote self-care and emotional well-being?

9. Reflect on a specific fear or phobia you developed as a child. Analyze the root cause of that fear and explore strategies for gradually facing and overcoming it.

10. Write a dialogue between your adult self and your inner child. Have a conversation about their needs, fears, and desires and discuss ways in which you can provide comfort and support.

11. Identify a negative pattern or behavior that you've noticed in your life. Trace it back to its origins in your childhood. How can you challenge and modify this pattern to promote healing and growth?

12. Write a forgiveness letter to someone who hurt you during your childhood. Focus on releasing any lingering resentment or anger and explore how forgiveness can contribute to your own healing journey.

13. Describe a comforting or soothing ritual you can create for your inner child. It could be a daily self-care practice, a visualization, or a symbolic gesture that brings a sense of safety and nurturance.

14. Reflect on a role model or mentor from your childhood who provided guidance and support. What positive qualities did they possess, and how can you embody those qualities in your own life?

15. Write down three things you appreciate and admire about your inner child. Celebrate their resilience, creativity, and ability to find joy in simple things.

16. Identify a core belief you hold about yourself that is no longer serving you. Challenge that belief by examining the evidence that supports a more compassionate and self-affirming perspective.

17. Describe a situation in which you felt invalidated or not heard as a child. How does that impact your communication and assertiveness as an adult? Explore strategies for expressing your needs and boundaries effectively.

18. Reflect on a significant loss or separation you experienced during your childhood. How has that impacted your ability to form attachments or trust others? Explore ways to cultivate healthy relationships and heal any emotional wounds.

19. Write a gratitude letter to your inner child, expressing appreciation for their resilience and strength in navigating difficult experiences. Acknowledge the lessons they taught you and the growth you have achieved as a result.

20. Imagine your ideal relationship with your inner child. Describe the qualities of that relationship and brainstorm ways to nurture and maintain it on an ongoing basis.

**YOUR INNER CHILD IS
WAITING FOR A GENUINE,
HEARTFELT APOLOGY.**

—YONG KANG CHAN

Chapter 5

Understanding Your Inner Child

NEXT, IT IS TIME to focus on getting to know your inner child with some more depth. Your inner child is a part of you, and because of that, they're someone that you need to learn to truly connect with, starting with the ability to identify inner child wounds.

Recognizing Inner Child Wounds

The tricky thing about recognizing inner child wounds is that they'll look a bit different for everyone. My inner child wounds are going to look different from yours. But there are still a few ways that you can identify inner child wounds. For example, mark off the signs on this checklist that may indicate inner child wounds:

- low self-esteem
- fear of abandonment
- trust issues
- emotional outbursts
- self-sabotaging behaviors
- difficulty setting boundaries

- repetitive relationship patterns
- inner critic and self-judgment
- feeling disconnected from emotions
- struggling with identity formation

If you have two or more of the aspects listed above, then there's a good chance that your inner child wounds are actively impacting your daily life. Some of the ways that inner child wounds can manifest include

- emotional challenges
- low self-worth
- relationship difficulties
- self-sabotage
- attachment issues
- repetitive patterns
- boundary problems
- inhibited growth
- fear and anxiety
- coping mechanisms
- sense of identity issues

The road to healing these inner child wounds isn't easy, but with the following activities, you can get much closer to your inner child, providing them with much needed compassion and healing.

Exercise No. 1 **Letter to Your Inner Child**

This first activity involves creating a letter for your inner child. Within you, they reside, just waiting for someone to notice them. What you are going to do is utilize the space below, and write them a heartfelt letter. Talk to them about the things that you think they need to hear, or things that you feel should be acknowledged. In your letter, offer them understanding, compassion, and reassurance. Talk to them and comfort them how you wish you had been comforted, and acknowledge the pain they've experienced.

Exercise No. 2 **Visual Timeline**

Part of understanding your inner child is being able to see the timeline of events that impacted them. Because of this, the next activity centers itself around a visual timeline. Starting with the first significant memory you have, leading up to the age of 18, construct a visual timeline using the line below or on another sheet of paper. Don't use words to do it, though—instead, use drawings, colors, and symbols in order to represent the events that your inner child experienced in each period of childhood, highlighting specific significant emotions and experiences.

After you've finished the construction of your visual timeline, reflect on the experiences your inner child had and see if you can notice any patterns in events or emotions that would have wounded your inner child.

Exercise No. 3 **Mirror, Mirror**

This activity is going to be a visualization and meditation activity, so make yourself comfortable and try to relax. I want you to start by closing your eyes and imagining yourself walking through a forest. Take note of how vibrant everything is around you as you suddenly stumble into a clearing. In the center of that clearing is a large tree, and it holds a magic mirror. Stand in front of the mirror, and gaze into it. Imagine a younger version of yourself transforming and taking your place in the mirror before your eyes. There they stand, at the exact significant age in which you faced some harrowing challenge.

With a curious and empathetic mindset in hand, imagine yourself stepping into the mirror to comfort them. Give them a hug and offer them compassion and comfort. Envision yourself telling your inner child about the strength you've gained and how their experience was hard, yes, but it also proved valuable. From it, you have been able to grow.

Before you head off, take the time to play with your inner child— do something joyful that they would enjoy. Using toys, art, games they love, and more, play with your inner child and notice how their face lights up and how happy they seem, glowing even. Hug them again and tell them that you are always there for them before stepping out of the reflection.

In the space below, journal about your experience. Take note of any significant emotions or events that came up and how you feel overall.

These three activities are all geared at helping you recognize your inner child wounds, as they can often be an elusive thing. I recommend going through each of these exercises before moving forward to connecting with your inner child because it is hard to connect with someone you don't understand.

Connecting With Your Inner Child

All of the following activities are geared at helping you further connect with your inner child, understanding their needs along the way. Take some time to interact with the following four activities in order to truly form a connection with your inner child!

Exercise No. 4 **Multiple Choice**

Answer the following multiple choice questions to get to know your inner child better, and jot down any notes in the margins.

1. What were your favorite hobbies or activities as a kid?

    a. Creative hobbies, such as dress up or imaginary games

    b. Physically active hobbies, like sports.

    c. Independent hobbies, such as reading or drawing

    d. Cooperative hobbies, like playing with other children

2. As a kid, which needs did you struggle with most?

    a. Emotions—having your emotions validated or comforted

    b. Physical—having enough food, water, or shelter to keep you safe

    c. Creative—being able to express who you are

    d. Connection—connecting with children, parents, and others

3. When did you feel most comforted as a child?

    a. When receiving physical affection, such as a hug

    b. When someone verbally comforted you

    c. When comforting yourself in some way

    d. When you were able to distract yourself from discomfort
    or sadness

4. Which of the following "child" activities still brings you
    immense joy? You may select more than one.

    a. Playing pretend

    b. Coloring

    c. Dress up

    d. Making creations like recipes, games, and art

    e. Playing games

    f. Telling stories

Based on your responses, you can tell a few things about your inner
child. You may know, for example, based on the fact that they felt
most comforted when alone, that they couldn't really rely on others
around them to comfort them, expressing the fact that your inner
child is not quick to trust others to support them. Analyze each of
your responses and jot down any observations you have below.

Exercise No. 5 **Fill in the Blanks**

Keeping with the theme of becoming more connected to your inner child, the following exercises are intended to help you get to know your inner child and connect with them further. Fill in the blanks or circle corresponding responses for each question.

1. When I was a child, I dreamed of becoming _____.

2. This (does/doesn't) align with what I'm currently doing because _____.

3. What I think my inner child would say about my current life is _____.

4. The part of my life my inner child would like best right now is _____.

5. The part of my life my inner child would like least right now is _____.

Again, use the space below to analyze and make note of any observations that arise as a result of your answers to the last questions.

Exercise No. 6 **Emotional Time Capsule Short Response**

In this activity, you'll be doing a bit of imagining! Envision that you have a magical time capsule transportation device. This device has the ability to transport you to any moment throughout your childhood. Which moment would you choose to revisit? Below, answer the following reflection questions:

- What moment did you choose and why?

- How did it make you feel?

- Is there anything you wish you could change about that moment?

_____

_____

_____

_____

_____

_____

_____

_____

_____

_____

_____

Exercise No. 7 **Matching Game**

Below, you will find two columns of statements/concepts. Match the ideas in list A to the ones in list B by determining which activities are indicative of which traits. This activity is geared at helping you identify traits of your inner child, things that they display through being their natural and curious self.

LIST A	LIST B
a) Curious and adventurous spirit b) Love for storytelling and imagination c) Emotional sensitivity and empathy d) Playful and carefree nature e) Creativity and artistic expression f) Need for love, comfort, and validation	i) Engaging in outdoor exploration and discovering new things ii) Getting lost in imaginative play and creating magical worlds iii) Feeling deeply for others and understanding their emotions iv) Laughing, running, and embracing the joy of the present moment v) Drawing, coloring, or engaging in any form of artistic expression vi) Craving affection, cuddles, and reassurance from loved ones

Creative Activities for Inner Child Bonding

Next up, I have three activities for you that will help you bond with your inner child. As we age, no matter how healthy of a childhood we had, everyone starts to lose touch with their inner child. But with these activities, you can begin to rekindle that connection between you and your inner child in a fun and interesting way.

Exercise No. 8 **Coloring**

I want you to go to the store, or even just connect up your printer, and obtain a few coloring pages or an entire coloring book. Get everything you need to color, whether it be markers, crayons, or something else—ideally, purchase the same tools you loved as a child. For this activity, you are going to be coloring. However, we're going to spice it up a bit. The rules for this coloring activity are:

1. There are no rules!

That's right! When you color, you are expected to stay inside the lines and match colors to what they are in real life, but for this activity, I want you to throw all of that out! Your inner child wouldn't care if you colored a duck green, so neither should you. Spend some time coloring in your pages spontaneously, without worrying about it being perfect or making sense. Just let your inner child take control, and see how it makes you feel.

Exercise No. 9 **Dress Up**

It is going to feel silly, but for this exercise, I want you to dress up so that you can truly embrace the creativity of your inner child. Now, as a child, you probably had way more options for dress up than you do as an adult. You had your own clothes, costumes, your parents' clothes, and even makeup at your disposal to do what you want to with—all without a care. But as an adult, you may have a perfectly curated closet—one that fits your lifestyle and profession. So this is going to take a bit of creativity.

I challenge you to go into your closet, makeup, or whatever else you have around the house, and craft the silliest outfits that you can. No, really—put them on and let yourself feel like a silly child again; your inner child will thank you. If you need some inspiration, try to use what you have in your closet to dress up as different professions, even ones that don't exist in real life!

Then, use this space to journal about how the activity made you feel:

_____

_____

_____

_____

_____

_____

_____

_____

_____

_____

Exercise No. 10 **Cooking**

Do you remember being a kid and wanting to eat silly meals that your parents would never let you have, like chicken nuggets for breakfast or sprinkles on mashed potatoes? Heal and connect to your inner child by doing that now. Go into your kitchen and challenge yourself by making silly, fun meals that you know your inner child would have loved, then sit down to eat. Forget all of the rules of cooking if you want to and just focus on having fun.

In this chapter, you spent time learning more about your inner child and truly connecting to them, forging a relationship that your inner child appreciates. Good work!

**THE FIRST STEP TOWARDS
GETTING SOMEWHERE IS TO
DECIDE THAT YOU ARE NOT
GOING TO STAY WHERE YOU ARE.**

—J.P.MORGAN

Chapter 6

Healing Your Inner Child With CBT

Now that we've had a bit of fun, let's talk a little bit more about the powers of CBT and what else you can use it for to amplify your inner child healing journey.

Cognitive Restructuring for Inner Child Healing

Cognitive restructuring is a powerful tool used within CBT. It allows people just like you to identify negative thought patterns—in the case of inner child healing, ones that stem from negative childhood experiences—in order to reframe those thought processes and truly catalyze the healing process. Self-blame, criticism, and limiting beliefs can all be restructured through this process, allowing you to break free of the shackles they leave behind. Some of the ways that cognitive restructuring can help you include

- allowing you to examine core beliefs to replace them with ones that are both more accurate and positive.

- helping you to distinguish between past experiences and the present reality.

- encouraging you to be compassionate toward yourself and find positive perspectives.

- aiding you in learning to cope with triggers and complementing other therapeutic techniques.

And much more! CBT and cognitive restructuring are tools that truly help individuals grow and foster self-discovery, as they create the ability for us to develop a positive mindset and reduce the impact that negative thought patterns have on us. Let's get into the exercises to help you out with this!

Exercise No. 1 Inner Child Mosaic

For this activity, you are going to be creating a mosaic—or collage—that represents your inner child. If you have or want to use your own paper, that's wonderful—but just in case, there is a blank space for you to use for your collage here as well. Otherwise, you'll need art supplies and collage materials, like markers, pens, paint, glue, old magazines, and whatever else you think you'll want to use. Once you have your materials collected, close your eyes and connect with the emotions and memories of your inner child. Once you feel that connection, create a mosaic of images, colors, and symbols that you feel best represent your inner child.

This exercise helps with cognitive restructuring because it allows you to see your inner child in a positive light. It can be really easy to blame ourselves for the negative experiences that we have, but the point of this activity is to help you see that you were just an innocent child—someone who loved bright things and beauty in life before bad experiences took that from you. Through this activity, you can reconnect to that part of you.

Exercise No. 2 Inner Child Time Capsule

This exercise is dedicated to providing you with somewhat of an inner child sanctuary. What you are going to do is set up an area in your home for this activity. It can be a room, a corner, or even a table! We're going to call it the Inner Child Time Capsule Adventure Zone. Decorate your space with a fun theme that you just know your inner child would love. You can do space-themed, princess-themed, or anything else that reminds you of your inner child. Then, grab some art supplies, notecards, paper, or anything else you think you may need.

Next, write notes to your inner child. Go back in time mentally and think about things your inner child needed to hear, like encouragement or comfort. You can even write down silly notes, jokes, doodles, or cute activities to engage with later. Put these activities and items in a box—such as a shoebox—and leave the box in this area, revisiting it when you have particularly rough times going on.

Exercise No. 3 **Your Dream Journey**

Below, you'll find several different panels. Imagine them like comic panels or storyboard panels. Inside of them, you are going to draw and write captions. "Of what?" I hear you ask. Well, it is simple! Imagine yourself on a dream journey where your adult self visits your inner child. What would you say and how would you interact? Fill in the panels with illustrations of key scenes, and include dialogue too!

Exercise No. 4 **Inner Critic to Inner Champion**

Next up, you are going to work on transforming your inner critic to an inner champion! In this activity, use the spaces below to write down a thought or statement that your inner critic would say. Then, write down a transformation of the thought into something positive. I've filled out the first row of the table for you so you can see how it is done.

Inner Critic	Inner champion
Ex: I always misunderstand what my friends are saying to me... I'm so stupid and such a bad friend!	Ex: My friends are always super understanding when I don't get what they're saying the first time; I'm so grateful to have wonderful friends! Ex: Sometimes, I need a bit of patience to understand things. That's just one difference that makes me unique!

The point of this exercise is to help you realize how your thoughts are your own creations, and it is up to you whether they will be critical or if they'll turn you into a true champion.

Coping With Trauma: Your Inner Child and You

These next exercises are all geared toward helping you and your inner child cope with trauma in some way.

Exercise No. 5 **Inner Child Map**

For this activity, you are going to create an inner child map of different spaces within your inner child's world. Use the space provided to create the following locations, getting as creative as you can:

- Courage Cove
- Empowerment Enclave
- Healing Harbor
- Any other spaces you think would be neat to add!

Color in your map, and make it appealing to you.

Now, you are going to engage in a visualization exercise. For each of the spaces you've designed, imagine how you can embody the theme of that space. So, for example, imagine you are in the Courage Cove. What can you do to truly embody courage, especially in times where it is hard? Do this for each location, then reflect below.

Exercise No. 6 **Inner Child Retreat Guided Meditation**

Imagine yourself walking in a serene forest, surrounded by lush greenery and the soothing sound of birds chirping. As you walk, notice a warm, gentle light filtering through the trees, illuminating your path. This light represents the healing energy that is always available to you. In the distance, you spot a small, playful version of yourself—the inner child that you hold so dear—waiting to greet you. They are the exact age you were when you faced your largest negative circumstance. Approach them with love and compassion, knowing that you are here to provide comfort and support.

Sit down with your inner child, and listen to what they have to say. Allow them to express their feelings and emotions without judgment, venting in the way that no one let you vent as a child. Let them know that you are here to protect and nurture them and that they are safe with you. As you hold a space for your inner child, visualize a loving, protective energy surrounding both of you like a warm, comforting embrace. This energy represents your ability to cope with trauma and to heal.

Now, ask your inner child what they need from you in order to feel safe and secure. Listen carefully and respond with kindness. You might hear them asking for love, reassurance, or simply someone to play with. Know that this is what you need most too, and don't force a response—just welcome whatever arises. As you fulfill their needs, notice the healing light in the forest growing brighter and more powerful. This light is the love and understanding you are offering your inner child.

Take a moment to remind your inner child that you will always be there for them. Promise to keep this connection open and return to this healing space whenever they need you. Now, slowly bring your awareness back to your physical surroundings. Wiggle your fingers and toes, and take another deep breath in, exhaling slowly. When you are ready, gently open your eyes. Carry the feeling of love and healing with you throughout your day, knowing that your inner child is safe, supported, and deeply loved.

Exercise No. 7 **Inner Child Affirmations**

Repeating affirmations to yourself is more effective than you might think! Every day for a week, I challenge you to look in the mirror and repeat three inner child affirmations to yourself and see how this impacts you over the course of that week. Take a look at these common inner child affirmations, then jot down some of your own below:

- I love and accept my inner child unconditionally.
- My inner child is safe and protected.
- I give myself permission to play and have fun.
- I am worthy of love and care.
- I allow myself to feel and process emotions.

_____

_____

_____

_____

_____

_____

Exercise No. 8 **Reparenting Your Inner Child**

As a child, it is not uncommon for events to be traumatic, even if looking back as an adult, they seem rather simple. This event is all about parenting your inner child once again but, this time, avoiding the trauma. Take a look at the list of common traumatic events that children face—some of which you may have experienced—and use the space below to write down what you would say to your inner child if they were in a similar situation.

- A child's parent consistently tells them they are worthless, stupid, or won't amount to anything, causing the child to develop low self-esteem and self-doubt.

- A parent spanks or hits a child as a form of discipline, leaving the child feeling frightened and unsafe around their parent.

- A parent emotionally withdraws from their child, rarely showing affection or interest in the child's life, leading the child to feel unloved and emotionally abandoned.

- A parent places relentless pressure on a child to achieve high grades or excel in sports, leading the child to feel immense stress and anxiety to meet their parent's expectations.

- A child lives with a parent who abuses drugs or alcohol, resulting in neglect, unpredictability, and feelings of instability in the child's life.

- A child's parent dismisses their emotions or concerns, telling them to "toughen up" or "stop being so sensitive," causing the child to feel invalidated and unsupported.

- A parent frequently compares a child unfavorably to their siblings or peers, leading to feelings of jealousy, inadequacy, and resentment.

- A parent invades a child's privacy, reading their diary or constantly checking their messages, leading the child to feel violated and mistrusted.

- A parent consistently shows favoritism toward one sibling over the others, causing feelings of rejection and rivalry among the children.

- A child witnesses one parent abusing the other, resulting in immense fear, trauma, and confusion for the child.

_____

_____

_____

_____

_____

_____

_____

_____

_____

_____

_____

_____

_____

_____

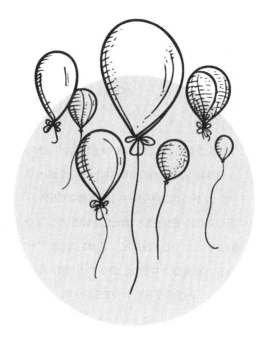

THE PROCESS OF RECLAIMING
YOUR WOUNDED INNER CHILD
IS A FORGIVENESS PROCESS.
FORGIVENESS ALLOWS US TO
GIVE AS BEFORE. IT HEALS THE
PAST AND FREES OUR ENERGIES
FOR THE PRESENT.

—JOHN BRADSHAW

Chapter 7

Maintaining the Healing Process

IT IS NOT ENOUGH to just work toward healing. All of that effort dissipates if you don't take steps to continue healing beyond the initial steps you do take. Working toward healing is a continuous, lifelong process that helps to foster emotional resilience and the ability to cope with stress. As you heal, you'll uncover more and more issues that need to be resolved, providing you with holistic healing. Moreover, healing these past wounds will benefit your future relationships and successes immensely. Let's take a look at how you can engage in continued healing.

Self-Care for the Inner Child

Let's start off with a look at how to engage in self-care for continued inner child healing!

Exercise No. 1 Self-Care Checklist

Taking care of yourself can be hard, especially if you don't have any ideas for how to do so. That's where this checklist comes into play! Use the following checklist to help you take care of your inner child, adding ideas to the end of it as well.

- Check in daily with your inner child's emotions and needs.
- Use positive affirmations to nurture your inner child.
- Engage in playful and creative activities.
- Express emotions without judgment.
- Set healthy boundaries to protect your inner child.
- Practice compassionate self-talk.
- Create a safe and comforting environment for your inner child.
- Prioritize sufficient rest and sleep.
- Seek positive social connections.
- Embrace your inner child's healing journey.
-
-
-
-
-
-
-
-
-
-
-

Exercise No. 2 **The Self-Care Menu**

The last checklist is great, but what if you need something specific when it comes to self-care for your inner child? This activity will help you curate a self-care menu!

Include activities for each category on the chart, creating your menu. If you want to make it more personal, copy your menu down on a piece of paper and add some design to it! This way, you'll always have an abundance of self-care ideas for any tone.

Nurturing activities	For bad moods
Creative activities	**Relaxation ideas**

Exercise No. 3 **Affirmation Cards**

Now, let's take a moment to make some fun and essential affirmation cards. For this activity, you are going to need some notecards and a box to keep them in. You can revisit the affirmations from earlier if you need some idea for what to put in your affirmation box. Write down affirmations that your inner child needs, and put them in the box. Keep the box in a safe yet easily accessible place so that you can pull it out in times of stress, allowing you to revisit those affirmations.

Continuing to Care for Your Inner Child

The following activities are directed toward helping you maintain your inner child healing through the power of routine.

Exercise No. 4 **Inner Child Journal**

Grab a journal or notebook—preferably a blank one—and designate it as your inner child healing notebook or journal. Each day or week, set aside time to talk to your inner child, connecting with them and them alone. Make it a special little routine, wherein you write letters to them, draw them pictures, or otherwise engage in various forms of self-expression.

Exercise No. 5 **Daily Affirmation Challenge**

Every day, state at least one affirmation to yourself either from the previous list or your affirmation box. Record below which affirmations you've used:

Exercise No. 6 **Self-Care Schedule**

Remember the self-care checklist and menu we worked with earlier? Now, it is time to plan self-care into your schedule. Take the time to set aside three dedicated times a week to engage in inner child self-care, writing these times down below.

_____

_____

_____

_____

_____

_____

_____

_____

_____

_____

_____

_____

_____

_____

With these routines and tools, you are sure to be able to continue the process of your inner child healing!

HEALING YOUR LOST INNER CHILD WOUNDING TAKES TIME, GENTLE CARE, AND LEARNING TO LOVE AND EMBRACE YOUR WOUNDED PARTS.

—ROBERT JACKMAN

Chapter 8

The Road Ahead

WELL, YOU'VE MADE IT! We're on the last leg of our journey together, and I can't be more proud of you. You've made it through so many stages of inner child healing that it is truly something to congratulate yourself for! Now, we're going to focus on a few more skills and activities that you can engage with to finalize your journey, giving you some additional ways to interact with your inner child.

Embracing Your Inner Child With Continued Work

Your inner child is the purest, most happy and free side of you. Your journey wouldn't truly be complete without embracing them with everything you have, accepting them and the role they play in your life, as well as the fact that they are fundamentally a part of you. Let's explore three final activities that will allow you to truly embrace your inner child with an open mind and heart, encouraging a lifetime of continued growth.

Exercise No. 1 Inner Child Art Exhibition

Bring those art supplies back out for another time! We're going to use them to create an inner child art exhibit. Now, if you have art and other projects from your childhood, that's great! You can include them in your inner child art gallery. But assuming that you don't have those—which is totally normal—you can create some brand new art that represents your inner child! Using colors, shapes, icons, and more, create art that you feel truly represents your inner child and their emotions, ambitions, and dreams. Hang your works of art up on the wall, even including description tags, as if they were part of a little art exhibition.

Something fun that you can do with friends is get together and engage in this activity together, taking turns guiding each other through one another's art exhibits and sharing what each work means to you. It is a fun and creative way to bond, inspire healing in others, and connect to your inner child.

Once you are done with your exhibition, you may want to take your works down. Of course, you can leave them up, but if you are taking them down, I recommend placing them somewhere safe. That way, if you ever feel like you are losing touch with your inner child, you can pull them back out and really connect.

Exercise No. 2 Creative Corner Setup

Most children have little play areas within their home. You may or may not have had one as a child, but either way, now is your time to establish a permanent play corner in your home—one where you can always turn to in order to be creative and interact with your inner child. Include art supplies, blankets and pillows, and anything else you think would be awesome to include when interacting with your inner child. If you don't have the space, once again, you can use a corner, closet, or even just a small table to dedicate to this practice. I highly recommend taking some time once a week to just be a child, engaging with your inner child in this creative corner you've built.

Exercise No. 3 **Nature Walks**

For most children, it is only second nature—no pun intended—to go out in nature and just observe. It is so carefree the way children engage with the world around them, and this is something that it is rather easy to lose touch with as we get older. Because of this, I suggest that you set a time either weekly or monthly to go for walks in nature that allow you to connect with your inner child. You can do this best by taking time to observe things with all five of your senses—excluding taste if you have to, because eating random things outside is clearly unsafe. As you venture, don't be afraid to collect rocks, acorns, sticks, and other items that your inner child would have picked up. You can even keep them in your creative corner to remind you of your fun adventure!

It is important to remember that, as you work toward healing your inner child, healing is non-linear. Sometimes, it is going to feel as though you've made no progress at all or even that you've done the reverse of making progress and have gotten worse! Rest assured that that is a normal feeling, and everyone encounters it when it comes to working toward healing. In these cases, the best thing that you can do is to keep your head up and continue to move forward, never letting little lapses in progress get you down. Much like Rome wasn't built in a day, progress doesn't happen overnight. Be kind to yourself. You're going to have to work continuously to heal your inner child, but in the end, I can promise that you'll be so glad you did!

Conclusion

THE JOURNEY TO SELF-HEALING is one that is going to take your entire life, but it is also one that is definitely worthwhile. While inner child work can be harrowing, upsetting, and even really hard at times, there's nothing like getting back to the state you were in before your trauma. When times get hard and you want to give up, remember that carefree, smiling child you once were—a child whose biggest issues were scraped knees and homework. Remember them and keep trudging forward, for them and for you.

Inner child work can be difficult, but with the skills you've developed throughout the course of this book, it doesn't have to be as scary or challenging as some can make it seem. Now, you have all of the tools necessary to successfully heal your inner child. All you need is time and a pinch of dedication. I promise you that you will never regret the steps you take toward healing.

In this book, you've added dozens of skills to your toolbox that will allow you to work toward healing your inner child. From the prerequisites of relaxation and focus all the way to CBT and IFS methods, you now have time-tested and psychologically proven skills to help pave the road to your success. You should pat yourself on the back for learning those skills and giving yourself the opportunity to heal.

Finally, as we close this book, I want to extend a sincere thank you. Thank you so much for trusting me to guide you along in this inner child healing journey; I know it is one that takes a lot of vulnerability, and you've taken a huge risk thus far. I am so proud of you and so appreciative that I could be part of your journey. If you found this book to be beneficial, consider leaving it a review! That way, other people just like yourself can have access to these extraordinary resources for healing.

Now, get out there and get to work. Start breaking down those cognitive distortions, reframing negative thought patterns, and healing that carefree and delightful inner child that lingers within you. You have what it takes, and I believe in you.

References

Aaron-Wayne, Lucille. (n.d.). *Seek deeply.* https://seekdeeply.com

Aaron-Wayne, Lucille. (2022, October 9). *How to do IFS on yourself, between sessions.* Seek Deeply. https://seekdeeply.com/how-to-do-ifs-on-yourself-between-therapy-sessions-blog-post/

Ackerman, C. (2017a, September 29). *Cognitive distortions: When your brain lies to you.* Positive Psychology. https://positivepsychology.com/cognitive-distortions/

Ackerman, C. (2017b, October 26). *Writing therapy: How to write and journal therapeutically.* Positive Psychology. https://positivepsychology.com/writing-therapy/

Aletheia. (2019, April 6). *25 signs you have a wounded inner child (and how to heal).* LonerWolf. https://lonerwolf.com/feeling-safe-inner-child/

American Psychological Association. (2021). *How to cope with traumatic stress.* https://www.apa.org/topics/trauma/stress

Austad, C. (2008). *Counseling and psychotherapy today.* McGraw-Hill.

Aybar, Susan. (2021). *4 somatic therapy exercises for healing from trauma.* Psych Central. https://psychcentral.com/lib/somatic-therapy-exercises-for-trauma

Bierbaum, N. (2018, December 11). *The three key elements of mindfulness.* Practical Mindfulness. https://practicalmindfulness.co.za/the-three-key-elements-of-mindfulness/

Bowdoin College. (2014) *Seeing thoughts as thoughts.* https://www.bowdoin.edu/counseling/pdf/seeing-thoughts-as-thoughts.pdf

Brainscape Academy. (2020, October 29). *10 focus exercises to build your attention span like a muscle.* https://www.brainscape.com/academy/focus-exercises-build-attention-span/

Cherry, K. (2022, August 10). *Cognitive behavioral therapy.* Verywell Mind. https://www.verywellmind.com/what-is-cognitive-behavior-therapy-2795747

Cherry, K. (2023). *What role do schemas play in the learning process?* Verywell Mind. https://www.verywellmind.com/what-is-a-schema-2795873

Cooks-Campbell, A. (2022). *How inner child work enables healing and playful discovery.* Better Up. https://www.betterup.com/blog/inner-child-work#

Crowe Associates. (2016, November 28). *Internal family systems model.* https://www.crowe-associates.co.uk/psychotherapy/internal-family-systems-model#

Cypress Lake Recovery. (n.d.) *Writing therapy.* https://www.cypresslakerecovery.com/treatment-modalities/writing-therapy/

Davis, A. (2023, January 3). *20+ inner child activities to heal and feel alive.* Ambitiously Alexa. https://ambitiouslyalexa.com/inner-child-activities/

Davis, S. (2020). *The wounded inner child.* CPSTD Foundation. https://cptsdfoundation.org/2020/07/13/the-wounded-inner-child/

The Decision Lab. (2023). *The ABC model.* https://thedecisionlab.com/reference-guide/psychology/the-abc-model

Earley, J. (2010, November 9). *A sophisticated approach to healing your inner child.* Personal Growth Programs. https://personal-growth-programs.com/a-sophisticated-approach-to-healing-your-inner-child/

Edmunds, E. (2017). *The 4 components of mindfulness (SOAP) – Mindful therapy for anxiety.* Freedom from Anxiety and Stress. https://drellisedmunds.com/2017/07/10/1458/

Fowler, P. (2018, January 11). *Breathing techniques for stress relief.* WebMD. https://www.webmd.com/balance/stress-management/stress-relief-breathing-techniques

Ginwright, S. (2020, December 9). *The future of healing: shifting from trauma informed care to healing centered engagement.* Medium. https://ginwright.medium.com/the-future-of-healing-shifting-from-trauma-informed-care-to-healing-centered-engagement-634f557ce69c

GoodTherapy. (n.d.) *Internal family systems therapy.* https://www.goodtherapy.org/learn-about-therapy/types/internal-family-systems-therapy#

Gotter, A. (2018, April 20). *What is the 4-7-8 breathing technique?* Healthline Media. https://www.healthline.com/health/4-7-8-breathing

Hestbech, A. M. (2018). Reclaiming the inner child in cognitive-behavioral therapy: the complementary model of the personality. *American Journal of Psychotherapy, 71*(1), 21–27. https://doi.org/10.1176/appi. psychotherapy.20180008

IFS Institute. (n.d.). *IFS directory.* https://ifs-institute.com/practitioners

IFS Institute. (n.d.). *Richard C. Schwartz, Ph.D. - the founder of internal family systems.* https://ifs-institute.com/about-us/richard-c-schwartz-phd

Integrative Psychotherapy. (n.d.). *An easy 6-step somatic process to process triggers.* https://integrativepsych.co/new-blog/somatic-therapy-five-towns

Kristenson, S. (2022, October 11). *13 signs you're dealing with inner childhood wounds.* Happier Human. https://www.happierhuman.com/inner-childhood-wounds/

Pederson, T. (2012, September 23). *How to heal your inner child: 10 self-soothing tips.* Psych Central. https://psychcentral.com/health/how-to-heal-your-inner-child

Pietrangelo, A. (2019, February 13). *Fear of abandonment: overview, symptoms, and treatment.* Healthline. https://www.healthline.com/health/fear-of-abandonment#

Psychology Tools. (n.d.). *Using Thought records to track & challenge thoughts.* https://www.psychologytools.com/self-help/thought-records/

Rizzo, A. (2021, April 10). *The 6Fs in IFS – The 6 steps to get to know our protectors.* Therapy with Alessio. https://www.therapywithalessio.com/articles/the-6-fs-in-ifs-the-6-steps-to-get-to-know-our-protectors

Rose, K. (2021, June 22). *25 fun & simple summer activities to heal your inner child.* Life with Kee Rose. https://www.lifewithkeerose.com/heal-your-inner-child/

Sanusi, M. (2021, July 29). *Healing is essential to liberation.* Health Resources in Action. https://hria.org/2021/07/29/healingandliberation/

Schupack, S. (n.d.). *Inner child work & IFS.* Sarah Schupack LMFT. https://sarahschupacklmft.com/internal-family-systems/

Schwartz, Richard. (2021). *No bad parts: Healing trauma and restoring wholeness with the internal family systems model.* Sounds True.

Skedel, R. (2021, December 15). *CBT for PTSD: How it works, examples & effectiveness.* Choosing Therapy. https://www.choosingtherapy.com/cbt-for-ptsd/

Sutton, J. (2022a, February 25). *Internal family systems therapy: 8 worksheets and exercises.* Positive Psychology. https://positivepsychology.com/internal-family-systems-therapy/

Sutton, J. (2022b, October 8). *Inner child healing: 35 practical tools for growing beyond your past.* PositivePsychology.com. https://positivepsychology.com/inner-child-healing/

Teule, E. (2015, March 10). *Reclaiming the gifts of your inner child.* Ekhart Yoga. https://www.ekhartyoga.com/articles/wellbeing/reclaiming-the-gifts-of-your-inner-child#

Tewari, A. (2022, October 14). *111 self-care affirmations for inner child, peace, and gratitude.* Gratitude - the Life Blog. https://blog.gratefulness.me/self-care-affirmations/

Villines, Z. (2023, April 25). *What is inner child therapy? Goals and what to expect.* MedicalNewsToday. https://www.medicalnewstoday.com/articles/inner-child-therapy

Zayed, A. (n.d.). *10 principles of cognitive behavioral therapy.* The Diamond Rehab - Drug & Alcohol Rehab in Thailand. https://diamondrehabthailand.com/cognitive-behavioral-therapy-principles/

Made in the USA
Monee, IL
19 April 2024

57179710R00089